D1438743

AGRICULTURAL

GE LIBRARY

ER, Glos.

-2 DEC

636.508512GR

COPY A

The
Nutrient Requirements
of
Farm Livestock

No. 1
POULTRY

TECHNICAL REVIEWS AND SUMMARIES

AGRICULTURAL RESEARCH COUNCIL
LONDON

1975

901025

First Impression 1975

Second Edition (Revised)

Published by the
AGRICULTURAL RESEARCH COUNCIL
and obtainable from
HER MAJESTY'S STATIONERY OFFICE
Government Bookshops
49 High Holborn, London WC1V 6HB
13a Castle Street, Edinburgh EH2 3AR
41 The Hayes, Cardiff CF1 1JW
Brazennose Street, Manchester M60 8AS
Southey House, Wine Street, Bristol BS1 2BQ
258 Broad Street, Birmingham B1 2HE
80 Chichester Street, Belfast BT1 4JY
or through any bookseller

Price £3.00 net.

Printed in England by
Henry Burt & Son Ltd, College Street, Kempston, Bedford

MEMBERSHIP OF THE WORKING PARTY
ON NUTRIENT REQUIREMENTS OF POULTRY

Chairman	A. EDEN, M.A. Ph.D., F.R.I.C.	Agricultural Development and Advisory Service
	*D. BALNAVE, B.Sc., Ph.D., F.R.I.C.	Queen's University, Belfast
	W. BOLTON, O.B.E., D.Sc., F.R.I.C., F.C.S., F.I.Biol., F.R.S.E.	A.R.C. Poultry Research Centre, Edinburgh
	A. W. BOYNE, B.Sc.	Rowett Research Institute
	PROFESSOR J. C. BOWMAN, B.Sc. Ph.D.	University of Reading
	*PROFESSOR W. O. BROWN, M.Agr., Ph.D., D.Sc., F.R.I.C.	Queen's University, Belfast
	MARIE E. COATES, Ph.D., F.P.S.	National Institute for Research in Dairying
	J. DAVIDSON, B.Sc., Ph.D., F.R.I.C.	Rowett Research Institute
	R. HILL, B.Sc., Ph.D., D.Sc.	Royal Veterinary College
	PROFESSOR D. LEWIS, M.A., D.Sc., F.R.I.C.	University of Nottingham
	PROFESSOR SIR ALEX ROBERTSON, C.B.E., M.A., B.Sc., Ph.D., D.V.Sc., LL.D., F.R.C.V.S., F.R.I.C., F.R.S.H., F.R.S.E.	Royal (Dick) School of Veterinary Studies
	K. L. ROBINSON, B.Sc., B.Agr., D.Sc., F.R.I.C.	Agricultural Research Council
	PROFESSOR T. G. TAYLOR, M.A., Ph.D.	University of Southampton
Technical Secretary	T. R. MORRIS, B.Sc., Ph.D.	University of Reading

*Professor Brown resigned in September 1970, following his appointment to the post of Chief Scientific Officer in the Ministry of Agriculture for Northern Ireland, and his place in the Working Party was then taken by Dr. Balnave.

ACKNOWLEDGMENTS

The Working Party is indebted to many companies and individuals who have supplied information and advice. In particular, it is a pleasure to acknowledge the co-operation of the British Turkey Federation, British United Turkeys Ltd., Cherry Valley Farms Ltd., BOCM Silcock Ltd., Spillers Ltd., and Sterling Poultry Products Ltd., and contributions made by Dr. R. Blair, Dr. K. N. Boorman, Dr. L. G. Chubb, Dr. W. A. Dewar, Dr. J. P. F. D'Mello, Mr. D. G. Filmer, Dr. C. Fisher, Prof. M. J. Head, Dr. D. Hewitt, Mr. W. S. Miller, Dr. H. Nott and Dr. D. H. Shrimpton.

TABLE OF CONTENTS

INTRODUCTION

In 1963 the Agricultural Research Council published the first of three volumes on the nutrient requirements of farm livestock, this being specifically concerned with Poultry. The Working Party responsible adopted the approach of reviewing the published information on each nutrient, with particular emphasis on the somewhat limited amount of work which reflected conditions in the United Kingdom in respect of breeds, husbandry and environmental circumstances and the types of feed and diets prevailing up to 1961. Inevitably the survey of the literature revealed some conflict of views on the requirements for poultry of each nutrient examined, even after disregarding experimental work known to have been complicated by health factors or appreciable nutrient imbalance. The procedure adopted in making recommendations was to select from the available range of figures the median value as the best estimate of requirement, unless circumstances justified a greater emphasis on a particular figure. In some nutrients the available information was too meagre to allow of any definite opinion and hence there were appreciable gaps in the recommendations.

Since the first Working Party completed its task there have been profound changes in the structure of the poultry industry in the United Kingdom. In the breeding field the vast production of hybrids for broilers and for egg production has followed upon the pattern of work in other countries, especially the USA, so that nutritional studies carried out elsewhere now have a greater relevance to conditions obtaining in the UK; these have at least considerably expanded the range of information available for review. Moreover there has been a vast expansion of experimental work with poultry in the United Kingdom in research institutes, universities, colleges and in commercial organisations, especially in the field of applied nutrition, which has added very materially to the literature available for consultation. Moreover, the greater availability of feeding stuffs during the last decade has enabled diets based on more precise nutrient standards to be tested on a much larger scale in circumstances equivalent to those obtaining in commercial practice. The increased intensification of poultry husbandry has allowed more critical examinations to be made of smaller differences in nutrient input and their interactions with environment, with consequent greater definition of optimum nutrient requirements. In short, the present Working Party has had much more information on which to base its findings than had its predecessors.

This greater availability of relevant information from both home and abroad has resulted in a much expanded text, thus bringing the present report more in line with the second and third of the ARC publications, which dealt with the nutrient requirements of Ruminants and Pigs respectively. In the field of nutrition today the problems of availability of nutrients in ingredients and of interaction of nutrients are assuming increasing importance. Such problems are magnifying the difficulties of assessing requirements of a particular nutrient in absolute terms without due regard for the concentration of other ingredients. Where, despite careful consideration of all available relevant literature, it was impossible to derive exact estimates of requirement of particular nutrients for a specified purpose the Working Party decided to give "preferred estimates" although these are necessarily subjective.

The problem of what constitutes a "requirement" as opposed to an "allowance" is not easy to resolve. In the previous edition, requirement was defined as the quantity of a nutrient or of energy, that should be supplied in the diet to meet the net requirement of the bird. The net requirement of a normal healthy bird is the quantity of a nutrient or of energy that it should absorb, given a completely adequate diet in an environment compatible with good health, in order to meet its needs. These needs may be for maintenance including the replacement of endogenous losses, for a specified growth rate, for a stated level of production or for reproduction.

The use of nutrient requirement values in the construction of practical diets may involve some allowance for natural variations in the nutrient content of ingredients, uncertainties concerning nutrient availability, and possible losses during manufacture and storage of the feed. Thus, it is common practice to formulate poultry diets with allowances for some vitamins and trace minerals in excess of the stated requirement. This practice may be justified when the cost is small and the element of doubt about the optimum dose is substantial. However, in the case of the amino acids and the major minerals it is not advisable to adopt such an approach and the terms "requirement" and "allowance" should be treated as synonymous. The formulation of practical diets is a matter for official and commercial feed advisory services, and must involve factors, including economics, that extend beyond the remit of the Working Party. For the present purpose the Working Party has adhered to presenting nutrient requirements in the sense defined above.

A. EDEN

Chairman, Working Party on the
Nutrient Requirements of Poultry

DEFINITIONS and CONVERSION FACTORS

With few exceptions, Système Internationale (SI) units have been used throughout this report, for the reason that these will progressively become the normal units for purposes of trade as well as for scientific communication. Factors for use in converting metric to Imperial units are given below; many of these will already be familiar to users of this book. The unit of energy in SI is the joule (1 joule $= 1$ kg m^2 s^{-2}) and this will gradually become the standard unit for expressing dietary energy concentrations. However, because of the comparative unfamiliarity of the joule in both nutritional science and agriculture at the present time, measures of energy are expressed throughout the text in calories, followed in brackets by the equivalent measurement in joules.

Dietary concentrations of nutrients are given as g/kg or mg/kg and refer to air-dry diets unless the contrary is stated.

Weights

1 kilogram (kg) $= 1,000$ grams (g) $= 2 \cdot 205$ pounds (lb)
1 g $= 1,000$ milligrams (mg) $= 1,000,000$ micrograms (μg)

Energy

1 Megajoule (MJ) $= 1,000$ kilojoules (kJ) $= 1,000,000$ joules (J)
1 calorie (cal) $= 4 \cdot 184$ joules (J)

The metabolizable energy (ME) of a diet is the energy contained in the feed ingredients which can be released and used for metabolic purposes in the tissues of the animal. It is normally estimated as the heat released on combustion of unit weight of a diet *minus* the heat released on combustion of the corresponding faeces, urine and gaseous products of digestion (if any).

Vitamins

Vitamin requirements are given in this report in international units, although this method of expression will eventually be superseded by definition of vitamin equivalents in units of mass.

Vitamin A. Vitamin A activity may be provided by the preformed vitamin in the form of its alcohol (retinol), esters or aldehyde (retinal), or by its "pro-vitamins", i.e. those carotenoids that can be converted to vitamin A in the animal body. One i.u. is the activity contained in $0 \cdot 3 \mu$g retinol or $0 \cdot 344 \mu$g retinyl acetate.

Vitamin D. 1 i.u. is the activity contained in $0 \cdot 025 \mu$g vitamin D_3 (cholecalciferol). Vitamin D_2 (ergocalciferol) is very much less potent as an antirachitic agent for poultry.

Vitamin E refers to members of the tocopherol group. 1 i.u. vitamin E is the activity contained in 1 mg synthetic dl-α-tocopheryl acetate.

3

Vitamin K occurs in several natural and synthetic forms, of which the most important are vitamin K_1 (phylloquinone), vitamin K_2 (menaquinone −7) and the synthetic vitamin K_3 (menaphthone). Their relative biological potencies are discussed in Chapter 4.

Vitamin B₆ refers to pyridoxol (2-methyl-3-hydroxy-4, 5-di(hydroxymethyl)-pyridine) or its corresponding 4-aminomethyl (pyridoxamine) or 4-formyl (pyridoxal) analogues. The term "pyridoxine" may be used to describe the naturally-occurring pyridine derivatives with vitamin B_6 activity.

Vitamin B₁₂ is used in the text to describe any cobalamin having biological activity for poultry. Cyanocobalamin is the commercially available compound most frequently used to provide a dietary supplement of vitamin B_{12}.

Folic acid is a group name for the naturally-occurring pteroylglutamic acids. It includes pteroylmonoglutamic acid (folacine), pteroyltriglutamic acid and pteroylheptaglutamic acid.

4

CHAPTER 1

REQUIREMENTS FOR ENERGY

INTRODUCTION

It is reasonably straightforward to identify as nutrients certain substances within the protein, mineral and vitamin fractions of the diet; it is also possible to regard water and certain unsaturated fatty acids as chemically definable materials which are needed in the diet. Although much of the fat and carbohydrate portions of the diet undergo biochemical oxidation within the animal they cannot be considered as contributing solely to this function since considerable amounts of these substances act only as potential energy sources when deposited in the body during growth. However, since the biochemical, physiological and physical activities of the animal lead to an energy expenditure it is convenient to relate this to a dietary requirement in terms of the dietary energy available to the animal. Within this concept, energy can be regarded as a nutrient and for poultry the total dietary energy available is conveniently expressed in units of metabolizable energy (calories or joules per unit weight). Metabolizable energy (ME) refers specifically to that portion of the dietary energy which is available to the animal for the production of meat and eggs and for the maintenance of body temperature and other vital functions.

It is important to recognise that, while there can be different yields of energy from the utilization and oxidation of different amino acids, carbohydrates or lipid materials, a given mass of an amino acid or a vitamin generally supplies the same amount of a particular nutrient and it is seldom possible to obtain a more or a less concentrated form. Therefore, it is now generally accepted that certain nutrients should be supplied in proportion to the requirement for energy and thus in proportion to the ME content of the diet.

There is no reason to regard energy supplied in the form of amino acids as being in any way different from that supplied by carbohydrates and fats since their total available energy content can be used both in anabolic and oxidative processes.

Carbohydrates form the major source of energy in all diets except those containing very high levels of fat. The subject of carbohydrate metabolism in the fowl has been reviewed (Vohra, 1967; Pearce and Brown, 1971). Experimental work has shown that there are wide differences in digestibility between the various classes of compound that make up the carbohydrate complex. However, it is accepted that the energy values of different ingredients, varying in the nature of their carbohydrate components, are best expressed in terms of metabolizable energy although there may be differences in the efficiency of utilization of this component depending on the type of production and the nature of the carbohydrate present (Burlacu, Grossu, Marinescu, Baltac and Grunca, 1969; Shannon, Waring and Brown, 1969).

Fats provide the most concentrated form of energy in the diet, but it is recognised that different fatty materials cannot all be ascribed the same ME value. The factors influencing the ME value have been reviewed by Edwards (1969). There is some uncertainty as to whether the efficiency of utilization of ME from fat is superior to that from a carbohydrate source. Generally with laying hens there has been no indication of an improved utilization of ME from fat for egg production (Waring, Addison and Brown, 1968; Balnave, 1971); but with growing chickens the substitution of fat for carbohydrate has usually resulted in an improvement in the efficiency of ME utilization, although not all fats are equally effective. Carew (1961) observed that increasing the proportion of vegetable fat at constant ME intakes resulted in an improved efficiency of ME utilization and the results of Shannon and Brown (1969a) and Gosling (1970) suggest that the heat increment for vegetable fat is less than for carbohydrate materials. However, it is not practicable to recommend that an allowance should be made for the higher net energy value obtained when ME is supplied in the form of fat or oil.

Birds are homœothermic and it has generally been accepted that for homœotherms an optimal environmental temperature range exists, known as the zone of thermoneutrality, over which metabolism is minimal. However, the position and extent of this zone is dependent on a number of factors including age (Barott and Pringle, 1946), acclimatisation to the environment (Gelineo, 1964; Shannon and Brown, 1969b) and genetical considerations (O'Neill, Balnave and Jackson, 1971).

Since most classes of poultry are given unlimited access to feed and since it is generally recognised that there is a degree of regulation of intake in terms of energy, the question of energy requirements is usually bound up with appetite. It is convenient to deal first with appetite and estimates of energy intake under *ad libitum* feeding conditions, and subsequently to consider controlled feeding conditions.

APPETITE

Appetite or voluntary feed intake is the amount of feed which an animal will consume when it has unlimited access to a diet. This voluntary intake presumably arises from a need to derive nutrients and energy from the diet to maintain body function both in terms of body temperature and body tissues. Since most classes of poultry are fed *ad libitum* it is important that the nutritionist should have reliable information about the expected appetite of birds for which he is required to formulate diets. In many cases the optimal concentration of nutrients in the diet will vary inversely with appetite. If the appetite of a flock is below the estimated level the birds may encounter nutritional deficiencies, and if appetite is higher than expected this will lead to some nutrients being consumed in larger quantities than are necessary with consequent waste.

The mechanism controlling appetite is complex and attempts to explain it in terms of a single factor, such as the level of blood sugar, have been unsatisfactory. It is clear that, at least when feeding diets of the kinds that are typical in the UK, feed intake is not limited by physical factors such as the distension of the crop or filling of the gizzard. Overall control is exercised by the hypothalamus, but the nature of the information which is acted upon by the hypothalamus and the pathways by which it transmits instructions to eat or not to eat are still incompletely understood (Mayer and Arees, 1968; Bell, 1971; Hervey, 1971; Boorman, 1973).

The effect of appetite control in the adult is to ensure that in the long term there is an overall balance between energy intake and energy requirements, perhaps with small excesses or deficits which are absorbed by increasing or decreasing the stores of body fat. In the growing animal there is some reason to think that appetite is a primary factor determining growth rate; but there is no completely satisfactory way of showing whether an increase in feed consumption (as induced, for example, by administering an oestrogen) is responsible for an increase in growth rate, or whether an increase in growth potential causes a change in appetite.

The many factors which influence voluntary feed intake can be divided into three main categories, depending on whether they arise from the bird itself, from the nature of the diet, or from the environment.

Differences between birds

Of the factors arising from the bird, clearly the most important are body size and rate of liveweight gain or output of eggs. Birds with larger bodies to maintain will require more feed for maintenance purposes and a fast growing chick can be expected to eat more feed than a slow growing chick starting from the same initial liveweight. It might be thought that the faster growing chick or the high producing hen could achieve its better performance by a more efficient utilization of its feed, but all the evidence indicates that any differences in metabolic efficiency are small compared with the contribution made by variable feed intake.

Effect of diet

The major dietary factor which affects feed intake is the concentration of energy which is normally expressed in terms of metabolizable energy (ME). Since the appetite mechanism is primarily concerned with long-term energy balance, increases in dietary energy are usually associated with decreases in appetite and *vice versa*. Indeed the bird might be said to have an appetite for energy rather than for feed, since the daily intake of energy is more nearly constant than the daily intake of feed by weight. This relationship between appetite and metabolizable energy content of the diet is considered in more detail on page 16.

The concentration in the diet of nutrients other than energy-yielding nutrients does not influence appetite so long as the level does not go outside the range which is acceptable for normal health and production. For example, increasing the level of protein or vitamins in a diet above the minimal requirement does not usually have an effect upon appetite, although ultimately a level may be reached at which toxic effects begin to appear. If the diet is deficient in one or more essential nutrients appetite is depressed, but this is associated with a decline in growth or reproductive performance. If the deficiency is extreme the animal may totally refuse to eat the diet. In the case of a marginal deficiency of an amino acid, both hens and chicks will sometimes consume extra feed so as to restore their intake of the limiting amino acid to an adequate level. In this case an appetite for the amino acid over-rules the appetite for energy, but the effect is a small one and occurs only when the concentration of the amino acid in the diet is close to the level needed for maximum performance.

Acceptability of the feed is a less important factor with poultry than with other classes of farm livestock, probably because the senses of taste and smell are not well developed in birds. Physical texture and appearance have some effect on the willingness of birds to approach and consume feed and this is particularly important with young chicks and turkey poults. The intake of very finely ground or dusty feeds is often a little lower than that of a coarsely ground mash.

When feed is offered in the form of pellets or crumbs there is a substantial increase in appetite compared with the intake of a mash. Table 1.1 lists some examples of increased feed intake which have been recorded for chicks and layers showing that the effect is of the order of 6% to 8% in most cases. In the young growing animal this increased intake is associated with a higher growth rate. In adult birds, rate of lay is unaffected and the increased nutrient intake is accounted for by a small increase in egg size and a relatively large increase in body fat.

Table 1.1
Effect of pelleting the diet on the voluntary feed intake of chicks and laying hens

		Feed intake (g/bird day)		Extra feed intake due to pelleting
		Mash	Pellets	
Chicks				
Allred, Jensen &	(expt 4)	25·0	27·1	8·4%
McGinnis (1957)	(expt 5)	25·5	27·3	3·0%
Allred, Fry, Jensen & McGinnis (1957)		20·8	22·8	9·9%
Bayley, Summers & Slinger (1968)		24·3	26·7*	9·9%
Layers				
Black, Jennings & Morris (1958)		147	152	3·4%
MacIntyre & Jenkins (1955)		134	142	6·0%
Petersen, Sauter,	2·35 kcal ME/g	130	137*	5·4%
Conrad & Lampman (1960)	2·93 kcal ME/g	122	126*	3·3%
Arscott, Rose &	2·50 kcal ME/g	111	115	3·6%
Parker (1962)	3·08 kcal ME/g	102	111	8·8%
	2·53 kcal ME/g	128	137*	7·0%
	2·64 kcal ME/g	124	134*	8·1%
Lee (1969b)	2·75 kcal ME/g	122	130*	6·6%
	2·86 kcal ME/g	121	128*	5·8%
	2·97 kcal ME/g	119	124*	4·2%

* These diets were pelleted and then broken down to form a "crumb" before feeding.

Effect of environment

The major environmental factor influencing appetite is temperature. It is clear that, in general, feed intake decreases as environmental temperature rises and that this is primarily a result of the lower energy requirements associated with lower heat losses from the body. At temperatures above about 30°C feed intake falls off more rapidly because the bird begins to have difficulty in eliminating all the heat associated with the metabolism of a normal feed intake. This decline in feed intake at high temperatures can lead to depressed growth or egg production, but tolerance of high temperatures is very much influenced by acclimatisation. Humidity and wind speed also have marginal effects. Estimates of the extent to which appetite changes with environmental temperature are given on pages 17 and 18.

Light intensity and day length have some effect on voluntary feed intake. With laying birds, photoperiod and light intensity both affect egg production and differences in feed intake appear to be consequences of differences in egg yield. For chicks. light has a more direct effect upon feed intake by regulating the pattern and extent of feeding activity. Maximum feed intake and growth rate are obtained when chicks are reared with continuous light (Morris, 1967).

Disease can reduce the appetite of poultry quite dramatically. It is also thought that feed intake can be increased by some parasitic infections of the intestine but the evidence on this point is not clear. Birds suffering from heavy intestinal infections certainly eat an excessive amount of feed *in relation to their performance*, but whether their appetite ever exceeds that of normal healthy birds is uncertain.

Many features of general management, such as the provision of adequate trough space and the density of stocking can also influence feed intake. Although these are more properly regarded as factors which affect the bird's opportunity to satisfy its appetite, their effect is the same as a genuine reduction in appetite when the formulation of a diet appropriate for these circumstances is considered. Allelomimetic behaviour, in which birds copy the feeding activity of their neighbours, can affect the pattern of feed intake and may also tend to increase the level of feed intake in some social situations.

ESTIMATES OF METABOLIZABLE ENERGY INTAKE

BROILER CHICKS

Broiler breeding programmes have as their principal objectives an increase in early growth rate and improvement in the yield of meat per unit of liveweight. The search for such improvements is continuous so that in attempting to construct input/output curves only the results of recent experiments are of value. Unfortunately, the time between the completion of an experiment and

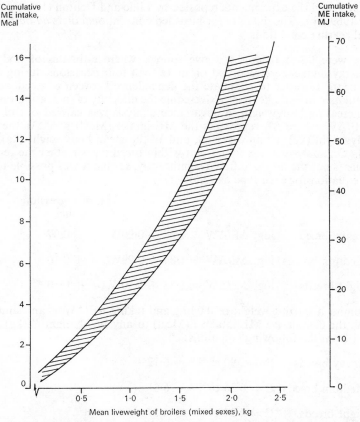

Fig. 1.1. Energy intake of broiler chickens expressed as a function of liveweight. Upper and lower lines represent minimum and maximum efficiency as observed in broiler flocks reaching mean liveweights of 2·0–2·5 kg at 9 weeks of age.

its publication can exceed two years; but the results from the breeder's own trials are usually available to him more rapidly than this.

Leading broiler breeders were therefore asked to supply weekly liveweights from 0 to 10 weeks for their own stock and weekly feed consumptions for the same period. The ME contents of the diets fed were generally not known and so the major suppliers of commercial diets were asked for the ME contents of their broiler feeds. Their replies indicated that broiler starter diets in use in the UK in 1970 contained about 2·95 Mcal (12·3 MJ) ME/kg and finishing diets about 3·04 Mcal (12·7 MJ) ME/kg. These values have been used to convert feed intake into energy intake.

The results of the exercise are set out in Figure 1.1 where cumulative ME intake is plotted against liveweight. The strains were not equally efficient and the hatched area shows the spread of values obtained.

GROWING PULLETS

Few published data are available on this topic and the present data have been obtained from four sources, namely a thesis by Lee (1969a) the estimates of Hill (1969) and the experiments reported by Lillie and Denton (1966) and Wells (1967; 1969a, b). The data are for birds fed conventional diets *ad libitum* under normal rearing conditions.

Data were taken from the above sources where estimates of bodyweight and energy intake were recorded on more than four occasions during a single experiment. In order to eliminate the dependence between consecutive values of cumulative ME intake, and to overcome the difficulty of increasing variability with increasing bodyweight, a covariance analysis was carried out of W and $\log_e \Delta E/\Delta W$, where ΔE represents the ME intake (Mcal) and ΔW the change in bodyweight (kg) within a period, and W the mean bodyweight (kg) in that period. On analysis it was found that within breed types neither the regression coefficients nor the means differed significantly, so that it was possible to give a single equation for each type as follows:

		SE of regression coefficient
Heavy breeds	$\log_e \Delta E/\Delta W = 1·67 + 0·90W$	$\pm 0·07$
Medium breeds	$\log_e \Delta E/\Delta W = 1·84 + 0·99W$	$\pm 0·10$
Light breeds	$\log_e \Delta E/\Delta W = 1·73 + 1·30W$	$\pm 0·10$

Assuming a starting weight of 0·04 kg and taking $\Delta E/\Delta W$ as an estimator of dE/dW, the cumulative ME intake E(Mcal) to any bodyweight W(kg) may be derived from the following equations:

Heavy breeds $\quad E = 5·90\ e^{0·90w} - 6·12$

Medium breeds $\quad E = 6·36\ e^{0·99w} - 6·61$

Light breeds $\quad E = 4·34\ e^{1·30w} - 4·57$

The curves derived from these equations are plotted in Figure 1.2 along with the actual experimental data obtained from the quoted references.

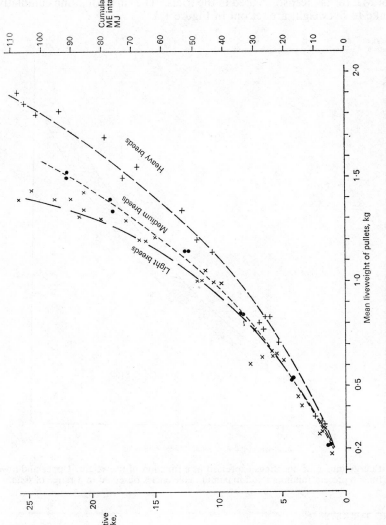

Fig. 1.2. The observed intake of metabolisable energy of growing pullets fed *ad libitum*, expressed as a function of liveweight.

11

DUCKLINGS

Weekly records of liveweight and feed consumption for ducklings were not available from UK sources. The liveweights and feed consumption values given by Snyder (1959) and Cornell University (1967) for birds aged eight weeks are in agreement with those obtained in the UK and their weekly data were used. The weights of feed eaten were transferred to energy intakes by using tabulated values of ME for the feedstuffs used in the trials. The curves relating cumulative ME intake to liveweight are set out in Figure 1.3.

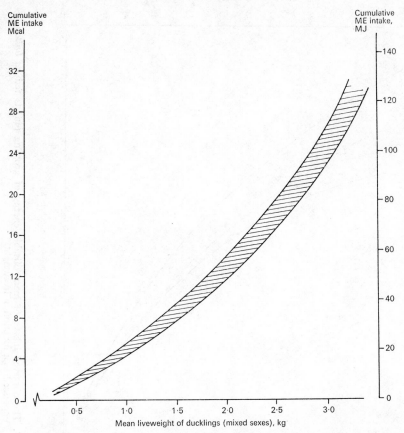

Fig. 1.3. Energy intake of ducklings expressed as a function of liveweight. Upper and lower lines represent minimum and maximum efficiencies observed in a range of data.

GROWING TURKEYS

Energy intake data have been obtained from turkey growth trials conducted in the UK, and from two Canadian experiments with Large White turkeys (Summers, Pepper, Moran and McConachie, 1968; Moran, Summers and Orr, 1969). Although there are some differences in growth rate between the stocks used in these various trials, the relationship between liveweight and ME intake is very similar in all cases.

Figure 1.4 is drawn from the data of Moran *et al.* (1969). This can be taken as representative of the energy intakes to be expected of rapidly growing turkeys

12

reaching liveweights of the order of 10 kg in the case of males and 7 kg in the case of females at 20 weeks of age. Slower growing strains would presumably require a somewhat higher energy intake to reach a given liveweight and, for any particular strain, intakes may be altered by changes in the dietary energy concentration which have the effect of advancing or retarding the finishing age.

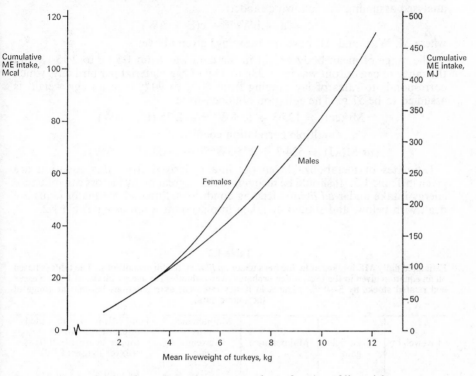

Fig. 1.4. Energy intake of growing turkeys expressed as a function of liveweight.

LAYING HENS

There have been a number of reports giving estimates of the effects of body weight and egg production on feed intake of laying hens under *ad libitum* feeding conditions. The best known of these is that of Byerly (1941) which, when modified by assuming an energy concentration in the diet of 2·90 Mcal (12·1 MJ) ME/kg, takes the following form:

$$M = 138 \ W^{0 \cdot 653} + 3 \cdot 29E + 3 \cdot 265 \Delta W$$

where   M = ME intake (kcal/bird day)

W = mean body weight (kg)

E = egg output (g/bird day)

Δ W = change in body weight (g/bird day)

Byerly's equation has been found to give satisfactory predictions of energy intake in many situations, but it has been considered worthwhile to derive a new equation from more recent data. Results from random sample laying trials and from feeding experiments published in the period 1965-1969 have been assembled to provide estimates of *ad libitum* feed intake and hence, by calu-

13

culation, energy intake averaged over periods of 8 to 12 months. The collection of data was limited to trials conducted in the UK so as to avoid the rather wider variation in diets and climatic conditions which would be introduced if North American data were included. Results have only been included if the diet was composed of commonly used feedstuffs and contained 140 to 165 g crude protein/kg and 2·4 to 3·0 Mcal (10·0 to 12·6 MJ) ME/kg. The data were analysed assuming the following model:

$$M = a + bW^{0·75} + c(E + \Delta W)$$

where M, W, E and ΔE have the meanings given above.

The range of mean body weight in the data was from 1·5 kg to 2·75 kg and the range of egg output was from 33g to 53 g of egg material per bird day, which corresponds to rates of lay ranging from 60% to 90% if mean egg weight is assumed to be 57 g. The equation obtained was:

$$M(kcal) = 125·3 + 65·8W^{0·75} + 2·75 (E + \Delta W)$$

(multiple correlation coefficient = 0·63)

$$or\ M(kJ) = 524·3 + 275·3W^{0·75} + 11·51 (E + \Delta W)$$

Estimates of metabolizable energy intake derived from this equation are given in Table 1.2. It should be recognised that a great many factors can influence energy intake under *ad libitum* feeding conditions. Some of the major items are dealt with below, and should be taken into account when using Table 1.2.

Table 1.2

Estimated daily ME intakes of laying hens under *ad libitum* feeding conditions. The table is based on an equation given in the text, which probably over-estimates the energy intake of Light Sussex and related stocks by 5-10%. Figures in italics represent extrapolations beyond the range of the source data.

Liveweight	Liveweight gain	Maintenance	Maintenance plus liveweight gain	Total ME intake for stated rates of egg output (upper figures: kcal/d) (lower figures: kJ/d)			
				Egg output, g/hen day			
		kcal/d (above)	kcal/d (above)	25	35	45	55
kg	g/d	kJ/d (below)	kJ/d (below)	(44%)*	(61%)	(79%)	(96%)
1·25	*1·0*	*203*	*206*	*275*	*302*	*330*	*357*
		849	*861*	*1149*	*1264*	*1379*	*1494*
1·50	1·2	214	218	*287*	314	342	369
		895	910	*1199*	1314	1429	1544
1·75	1·4	225	229	*298*	325	353	380
		941	957	*1247*	1362	1477	1592
2·00	1·6	236	240	*309*	337	364	392
		987	1004	*1293*	1408	1523	1638
2·25	1·8	246	251	*320*	347	375	402
		1029	1050	*1338*	1453	1568	1683
2·50	2·0	256	262	*330*	358	385	413
		1071	1095	*1382*	1497	1612	1727
2·75	2·2	266	272	*341*	368	396	423
		1113	1138	*1425*	1540	1655	1770

* Corresponding rates of lay if mean egg weight = 57 g.

Because Byerly used a different power of body weight and assumed an intercept of zero in his model, the coefficients of the two equations cannot be compared directly. However, the overall prediction of ME intake by the two equations within the practical range of body weight and egg output can be compared. When this is done, it is found that there is close agreement between the two equations although, for body weights greater than 2·5 kg, the equation derived from Byerly (1941) gives larger and increasingly divergent estimates of ME intake.

FACTORS AFFECTING METABOLIZABLE ENERGY INTAKE

As has been explained in the preceding section on Appetite, many factors can modify energy intake, but many of these are difficult to quantify in any useful way. However, there is detailed evidence about the two most important factors, environmental temperature and dietary energy, and these will now be dealt with in more detail.

ENVIRONMENTAL TEMPERATURES

Growing Chicks

The effects of environmental temperature on the growth rate and feed intake of growing chicks have been studied by a number of workers.

In experiments in which various constant temperatures have been compared, it has usually been found that low temperatures (12° to 18°C) give the best overall growth rates, but much higher temperatures (30° to 35°C) give maximum efficiency of feed conversion (Romoser and Helbacka, 1958; Pope, 1960; Milligan and Winn, 1964; Huston, 1965; Prince, Whitaker, Matterson and Luginbuhl, 1965). Prince, Potter and Irish (1961) reported a highly significant linear effect of temperature on efficiency of feed conversion with values of 0·351 g gain/g feed at 7·2°C and 0·395 g gain/g feed at 23·9°.

Howes, Grub and Rollo (1962) used steadily declining temperatures (−1°/d) but they also found that growth rate was best in the coolest environments and feed efficiency best in the warmest.

In each study, temperature was varied but the composition of the diet remained constant. It is known that the energy demand for maintenance decreases as the environmental temperature increases, but the demand for energy for growth, and for nutrients other than energy for maintenance and growth are unaltered. The experiments described above are therefore open to criticism. Until such time as experiments are carried out wherein the diet is so altered that only the energy intake alters with temperature, it would be unwise to make recommendations.

Laying hens

In the adult hen, feed intake decreases with increasing temperature; but egg output is not usually affected until mean ambient temperature exceeds about 30°C (or more in acclimatised birds) so long as the intake of nutrients *other than energy* remains adequate.

Payne (1967) has estimated that the decrease in feed intake associated with an increase in ambient temperature corresponds to a drop of 1·6 % for each 1°C rise in temperature. An attempt has been made to extend Payne's observations by

15

using recently published results. A summary of the data, including those given by Payne (1967), is shown in Table 1·3. Although there is a considerable variation in the estimate as derived from various sources, the data indicate a mean decrease in feed intake of 1·7% for each 1°C rise in environmental temperature within the range +7° to +35°C. The data of Romijn and Vreugdenhil (1969) were obtained with one bird only and so have not been used in estimating this mean figure. It should be recognised, however, that the reduction in feed intake may not be uniform throughout the range and that much more rapid declines in feed intake have been reported from experiments using environmental temperatures above 30°C (van Kampen and Romijn, 1970; Smith, 1971).

Table 1.3

Compound percentage reductions in feed intake of laying hens for each 1°C rise in environmental temperature

Source	Temperature range (°C)	Compound percentage reduction in feed intake for each 1° rise in temperature
Ota 1960)	− 5 to +13	1·6
* Ota (1960)	+13 to +29	1·3
Ota (1960)	− 5 to +29	1·5
* Mueller (1961)	+13 to +32	2·1
* Payne (1964)	+19 to +30	0·9
* Payne (1966)	+17 to +29	1·6
* Charles, Payne & Lamming (1963)	+18 to +29	2·0
Romijn & Vreugdenhil (1969)	− 9 to +20	nearly 0
Romijn & Vreugdenhil (1969)	+19 to +40	4·7
* Shannon (1966)	+22 to +28	2·9
* Davis, Hassan & Sykes (1970)	+ 7 to +35	1·0
Mean		1·7

* Data used in estimating the mean figure.

DIETARY ENERGY CONCENTRATION

Growing chicks

Chickens tend to adjust their daily feed intake so as to maintain an appropriate level of energy intake, with the result that the weight of feed consumed generally decreases when balanced diets of high energy concentration are offered. However, the adjustment made by the young chick does not usually compensate entirely for the change in energy content and so more concentrated diets lead to higher nutrient intakes with correspondingly higher growth rates. There may also be differences in carcass composition between groups of chicks fed diets with different concentrations of metabolizable energy.

16

If the energy content of a chick diet is increased (for example, by adding fat) without making adjustments to the levels of other nutrients, then growth rate may be limited by an inadequate intake of amino acids or minerals. For this reason it is important that an appropriate balance should be maintained between energy content and the levels of other nutrients both in practical diets and in experiments designed to investigate the effects of dietary energy. We have considered below only those experiments in which protein (or amino acid) levels were adjusted to maintain an approximately constant ratio with the level of dietary energy.

Chicks given diets with a high energy concentration generally grow more rapidly than those fed on less concentrated diets and this appears to alter slightly the amount of energy required to reach a given liveweight. Thus Smith (1967) compared diets containing 3·34 to 3·39 Mcal (14·0 to 14·2 MJ) ME/kg with diets containing 3·20 Mcal (13·4 MJ) ME/kg. From his results it has been calculated that males required 6·56 kcal (27·4 kJ) ME/g gain on the higher energy diet and 6·85 kcal (28·7 kJ) on the lower, and that females needed 6·69 kcal (28·0 kJ) ME/g gain on the high energy diet and 6·78 (28·4 kJ) on the lower. Insufficient information was given for the significance of these differences to be determined.

On the other hand, Combs (1968) summarised the results of several broiler trials where the diets contained energy levels ranging from 3·08 to 3·36 Mcal (12·9 to 14·1 MJ) ME/kg and reported that there were no measureable differences in the amount of ME consumed per unit liveweight gain within the range examined. This conclusion was confirmed by Andrews and Goodwin (1969) using diets whose energy contents were 3·07, 3·19 and 3·38 Mcal (12·8, 13·3 and 14·1 MJ) ME/kg.

The available evidence does not lead to any clear view about optimal or minimal levels of energy in diets for broiler chicks. The optimal level in any given situation will depend very much on the prices of feedstuffs; the minimal level depends upon the reduction in growth rate below the maximum which is acceptable in a particular set of circumstances.

The physical form of a diet (whether pellets, mash or crumbs) has a substantial influence on the resulting physical density and on growth (see Table 1.1). Although dietary energy concentration is normally expressed as energy per unit weight there is some evidence to suggest that energy per unit volume may be of value in defining the energy content of a diet, particularly at the lower end of the scale. Mraz, Boucher and McCartney (1956, 1957) observed that neither energy concentration nor physical density alone was satisfactory for measuring the adequacy of a diet for rapid chick growth and they preferred the use of an energy/volume measurement. Sibbald, Slinger and Ashton (1960) also observed that for young chicks nutrient concentration expressed on a gravimetric basis was not as satisfactory a measurement as nutrient concentration expressed on a volumetric basis.

Growing turkeys

Turkey poults, like baby chicks, tend to eat less as the concentration of nutrients in the diet is increased, but their ability to deal with low energy diets in mash form is very limited. Data from Atkinson, Kurnick, Ferguson, Reid, Quisenberry and Couch (1957) and from Auckland and Morris (1971) have been used to illustrate the important relationships in Figure 1.5. Clearly, the effect of energy concentration in the diet on energy intake and liveweight gain is important in the case of the turkey poult. However, the energy required per unit of liveweight gain is not markedly affected within the range of dietary energy concentrations from 2·2 to 3·6 Mcal (9 to 15 MJ) ME/kg, perhaps because of differences in carcase composition.

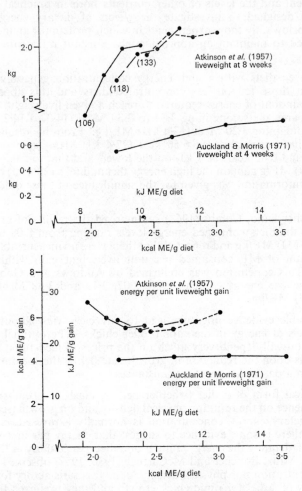

Fig. 1.5. The effect of energy content of the diet on liveweight gain of turkeys and on efficiency of energy utilization. The three lines given for Atkinson, Kurnick, Ferguson, Reid, Quisenberry and Couch (1957) refer to diets formulated with either 133, 118 or 106 g protein/Mcal ME.

Laying hens

It is known that ME intake can be increased by raising the energy concentration of the diet or feeding the ration in the form of crumbs or pellets. Although there have been some reports indicating that both growing and laying hens maintain constant energy intake when diets of widely differing energy levels are fed (Bolton, 1958; Hill, 1962; Foster, 1968) the reduction in feed intake which occurs at high dietary energy concentrations is generally insufficient to maintain a constant energy consumption and so energy intake and body fat

18

deposition tend to be greater at higher dietary energy concentrations (Morris, 1968; Waring, Addison and Brown, 1968; Jackson, Kirkpatrick and Fulton, 1969). Morris (1968) has shown that heavy breeds of bird are less able to control their energy intakes than light breeds.

The extent to which energy intake can be expected to change for a given change in dietary energy concentration is estimated in a general formula derived from a survey of published experiments by Morris (1968). As a rule-of-thumb, for a proportional increase in dietary energy content of x, energy intake will increase by about $0.5x$ in heavy breeds and $0.3x$ in light breeds. The extra energy is mainly converted to body fat. There may be some increase in egg weight but there is usually no increase in rate of lay (Morris, 1969).

If the diet is so low in energy that it entails a feed intake which exceeds the physical capacity of the bird, energy intake will then be inadequate to support normal egg production. From the evidence reviewed by Morris (1969) it would seem that the lower limit to dietary energy concentration is about 2·3 Mcal (9·6 MJ) ME/kg. Below this level one can expect reduced rates of lay if mash diets are fed. With pellets or crumbs the minimum energy concentration is almost certainly lower. The exact limiting value in mash diets is probably determined more by energy per unit volume than energy per unit weight.

The optimum concentration of energy in a laying diet is a matter which has to be determined by economic considerations. There is no "requirement" for dietary energy concentration under *ad libitum* feeding conditions, except that the energy content should be above the minimum concentration of about 2·3 Mcal (9·6 MJ) ME/kg.

ENERGY BALANCE AND ENERGY UTILIZATION

The estimates of energy intake given above are measures of what the animal voluntarily consumes under *ad libitum* feeding conditions. Another method of studying energy "requirements" is by direct or indirect animal calorimetry. This generally involves the use of small numbers of birds over short experimental periods, usually 24 hours, but the work is carried out under carefully controlled conditions with accurate recording of factors such as feed intake and temperature change. Calorimetric work also allows the estimation of heat output at different levels of feeding and thus the estimation of maintenance requirement for energy directly.

When estimates of energy requirements derived from calorimetric work, such as that of Waring and Brown (1965, 1967) and Grimbergen (1970), are compared with estimates of ME intake derived from laying trials it becomes obvious that there are wide discrepancies between data from the two sources. The estimates derived from the calorimetric studies are in the range from 75 to 85% of the energy requirements calculated from the laying trial data.

It is to be expected that with birds kept under normal management conditions the energy intake will be somewhat higher than estimates obtained using the more carefully controlled conditions in a calorimeter, but the difference between the two sources is rather high at 20%. This may be related to a number of factors including:

(i) Variable, lower temperatures under laying house conditions which would substantially increase the maintenance requirement.

(ii) Less accurate control of ME intake through scattering of feed and loss of feed in the drinkers under laying house conditions.

(iii) Loss of feathers during the course of a year spent in commercial battery cages. This loss may cause a substantial increase in heat output.

(iv) Variation in fasting metabolic rate with increasing age (Leeson and Porter-Smith, 1970). This may be related to feather loss (see iii), but the evidence for this is lacking.

(v) Greater activity under laying house conditions (although the birds may be more closely confined under commercial conditions, they are perhaps more active than an isolated animal in a calorimeter).

(vi) The inaccuracy involved in estimating mean bodyweight over an extended laying period.

(vii) A possible decline in the net efficiency of ME utilization under *ad libitum* feed conditions.

It is interesting to note that the requirements estimated by the calorimetric equations of Waring and Brown agree well with the ME requirements of hens under some laying house conditions (Brown, Waring and Addison, 1967) but this is not the general rule. The data of Balnave (1970) indicate that when White Leghorns are fed on a restricted basis the estimated ME intake derived from the calorimetric equation of Waring and Brown (1967) for a particular level of production is in the range 88 to 92% of the actual intake whereas when fed *ad libitum* the estimated ME intake is only 82 to 84% of the actual intake. Furthermore, when the data of Bolton (1958) are analysed it can be observed that, even when exceptional care is taken to measure accurately the *ad libitum* feed intake and weight of egg product formed over a full laying year, the estimated ME intakes derived from the calorimetric equation of Waring and Brown (1965) for Thornber 404 birds are only 78 to 82% of the actual intakes observed. These cases suggest that something other than feed wastage is responsible for the higher ME requirements observed under practical laying house conditions.

MAINTENANCE ME REQUIREMENTS OF ADULT FOWL

Table 1.4 gives the maintenance ME requirements of mature cockerels as derived from calorimetric studies. These data indicate a daily ME requirement of approximately 100 kcal (418 kJ)/kg$^{0.75}$ at 22°C. By analogy with the laying hen data the actual daily requirement for ME fed under normal management conditions is probably closer to 120 kcal (500 kJ)/kg$^{0.75}$.

Table 1.4

Daily ME requirement for maintenance of mature cockerels
(derived from calorimetric studies at 22°C)

Source	Bird type	Body weight (kg)	Daily maintenance requirement per kg$^{0.75}$	
			kcal ME	kJ ME
Shannon & Brown (1969a)	Light Sussex	4·0	97	405
O'Neill, Balnave & Jackson (1971)	Brown Leghorn	2·5	104	434
O'Neill (1971)	White Leghorn	1·9	102	425

Table 1.5 gives estimates of the maintenance ME requirement of the laying hen as computed from the experimental work of various authorities. Most of the data are extracted from Waring and Brown (1965). Apart from the different results obtained in laying trial and calorimetric investigations many other factors,

20

such as variations in environmental conditions and the breed and strain of birds used, will contribute to the range of results obtained from different sources. Furthermore, the variations in fasting metabolic rate observed by Leeson and Porter-Smith (1970) suggest that age might also be an important factor.

Table 1.5

Daily maintenance ME requirement of laying hens, derived either from regression analysis (regr) or respiration calorimetry (cal)

Reference	Body weight kg	Method	Daily maintenance requirement per kg$^{0.75}$	
			kcal ME	kJ ME
Titus (1928)	1·60	regr	119	498
Brody, Funk & Kempster (1938)	1·80–2·60	regr	122	510
Bird & Sinclair (1939)	2·90	regr	128	536
Byerly (1941)	0·68–3·29	regr	133	556
Bolton (1959)	1·81	regr	116	485
Waring & Brown (1965)	2·00	cal	106	444
Waring & Brown (1967)	1·70	cal	131	548
Grimbergen (1970)	2·00	cal	102	427
Leeson & Porter-Smith (1970)	2·25	cal	92	385
van Es, Vik-Mo, Janssen, Bosch, Spreeuwenberg, Vogt & Nijkamp (1970)	2·30	cal	105–115	439–481
Burlacu & Baltac (1971)	1·72	cal	126	527

The maintenance ME requirement of the White Leghorn hen (Waring and Brown, 1967) at 131 kcal (548 kJ)/kg$^{0.75}$ per day is surprisingly high when compared with the value of 106 kcal (444 kJ)/kg$^{0.75}$ per day obtained for the Thornber 404 hen by the same technique (Waring and Brown, 1965). Although the maintenance requirements per unit of metabolic body size were very different, little difference was observed in the efficiency of utilization of ME between the two breeds. Therefore, it is important to note that Grimbergen (1970) has indicated that even under fasting conditions laying hens utilize body reserves for egg synthesis with an associated heat loss. As this heat loss appears to be independent of body size the results imply that total heat production, including fasting heat production, need not be directly proportional to metabolic body size in hens.

The effect of environmental temperature on the maintenance ME requirements of adult fowl is shown in Figure 1.6. It is evident from these data that the maintenance requirements of both laying hens and cockerels decrease with increasing temperature. The result refers to animals which have been acclimatised at the appropriate temperature and do not describe the heat outputs to be expected in response to short-term changes in environmental temperature.

21

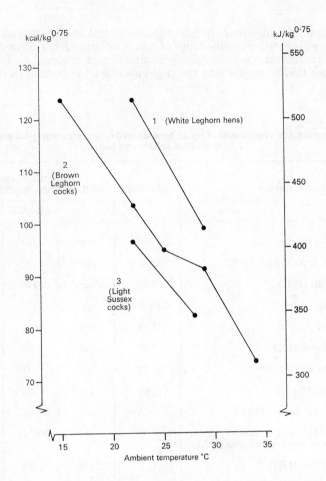

Fig. 1.6. The effect of environmental temperature on the daily ME requirements for maintenance (i.e. energy balance) of laying hens and cockerels. Key to sources: 1—Waring & Brown (1967); 2—O'Neill, Balnave & Jackson (1971); 3—Shannon & Brown (1969a).

EFFICIENCY OF UTILIZATION OF ME

Calorimetric studies of the effect of plane of nutrition on the energy balance of mature laying hens and cockerels have indicated that the efficiency of utilization of ME is constant at all planes of nutrition (Waring and Brown, 1965, 1967; Shannon and Brown, 1969a). As the ME content of a diet is known to be unaffected by variations in plane of nutrition from approximately 0·6 to 1·6 times maintenance it is evident that net energy and metabolizable energy represent constant proportions of the gross energy of a diet for a given purpose, e.g. maintenance or egg production. This implies that the digestive system of the fowl can deal efficiently with the digestion of carbohydrates, fats and proteins at levels of feeding up to its maximum food capacity.

Recent calorimetric estimates of the net availability of metabolizable energy from conventional and high-fat rations fed to laying hens and cockerels are given in Table 1.6. Few comparable data are available for growth, although Shannon and Brown (1970) observed that the net availability of ME at 22°C was 85·1% for 10 to 18 week-old broiler cockerels fed a high-energy broiler finishing diet. This efficiency for growth is similar to the efficiency for egg production in the laying hen and considerably higher than the efficiency for lipogenesis from carbohydrate sources in mature cockerels observed by these same workers. Burlacu, Baltac and Paraschiv (1970) reported that the efficiency of utilization of ME by growing Leghorn pullets was 78·1% at 3 months of age. No significant difference was observed between 2 and 5 months of age although at 1 month of age the efficiency was considerably lower at 66·2%.

Table 1.6
Recent calorimetric estimates of the net availability of metabolizable energy from conventional and high-fat rations fed to laying hens and cockerels

Source	Bird type	Temperature °C	Mean net availability of ME	Type of diet
Hens			%	
Waring & Brown (1965)	Thornber 404	23	83·7	conventional
Waring & Brown (1967)	White Leghorn	22	86·2	conventional
Porter-Smith & Shrimpton (1968)	Warren SSL	?	81·3	maize-soya
Grimbergen (1970)	White Leghorn	20	64·2	conventional
van Es, Vik-Mo, Janssen, Bosch, Spreeuwenberg, Vogt & Nijkamp (1970)	White Leghorn	?	80·0	conventional
Burlacu & Baltac (1971)	White Leghorn	25	78·5	conventional
O'Neill (1971)	White Leghorn	16 23 27 33	78·0 77·9 83·8 87·6	high-fat
Cocks				
Shannon & Brown (1969a)	Light Sussex	22 28	70·6 73·6	conventional
Shannon & Brown (1969a)	Light Sussex	22	84·1	high-fat
O'Neill, Balnave & Jackson (1971)	Brown Leghorn	15 22 25 29 34	65·5 67·9 70·6 73·1 78·9	conventional
O'Neill (1971)	White Leghorn	16 23 27 33	65·7 66·6 70·9 72·8	conventional

RESTRICTION OF ENERGY INTAKE

PULLETS OF EGG-PRODUCING STRAINS

Restriction during the rearing period

It is not the usual practice to restrict the feed intake of growing pullets being reared for egg production, but there is a substantial body of experimental

23

evidence indicating that feed restriction is beneficial (see Lee, Gulliver and Morris, 1971 for a review). The main advantage is a saving in the amount of energy required to reach point-of-lay. In addition restricted feeding reduces bodyweight at point-of-lay, delays the onset of sexual maturity and usually increases the mortality during rearing but decreases laying house mortality.

Although restricted feeding delays sexual maturity, subsequent egg production is normally increased and restricted birds generally show a higher peak rate of lay with a slower rate of decline thereafter. Total yield to a fixed finishing age is usually the same in full-fed and restricted flocks. A reduced percentage of small eggs is laid at the beginning of the production cycle following restricted feeding but mature egg size is similar to that of birds maintained on full-feed during the rearing phase. The age at the commencement of restriction and the duration of restricted feeding are important factors affecting the results of any particular programme (Fuller and Dunahoo, 1962; Gardiner and MacIntyre, 1962; MacIntyre and Gardiner, 1964). A common level of restriction has been 70% of *ad libitum* intake from 8 to 21 weeks of age. This reduces energy intake from 0–21 weeks by about 25%, although energy intake to 50% lay is reduced by less than 5%.

Restricted feeding during lay

Although restricted feeding in various ways during the rearing period may decrease bodyweight gain, and hence the maintenance ME requirement, without seriously affecting the resulting laying house performance, this benefit of reduced bodyweight at point-of-lay is rapidly lost when birds are placed on full feed in the laying house. Attempts have therefore been made to control excessive energy intake and bodyweight gain during the laying period, even for small-bodied laying strains.

Two methods employed include restriction of the quantity of feed offered to the bird and modification of the nutrient concentration of the diet through the addition of an inactive diluent such as wood dust or diatomaceous earth. Jackson (1969) has reported a series of experiments relating to both these methods of controlling the nutrient intake of the hen during the laying period and has reached the conclusion that actual limitation is the more effective method.

In some of the restricted feeding experiments energy alone has been restricted while the intakes of all other nutrients have been maintained at substantially similar levels (Combs, Gattis and Shaffner, 1961; Donaldson and Millar, 1962). However, the results obtained in these studies have been essentially similar to those in which all nutrients, including energy, have been restricted.

Restricted feeding of laying hens has consistently improved feed efficiency and decreased the rate of body weight gain (Sherwood, 1959; Combs *et al.*, 1961; Walter and Aitken, 1961; Donaldson and Millar, 1962; Balnave, 1969, 1970; Jackson, 1970) without seriously affecting mortality (Milby and Sherwood, 1956; Sherwood, 1959; Combs *et al.*, 1961; Sherwood and Milby, 1961). Although a decreased rate of egg production has often been observed as a result of restricted feeding (Sherwood, 1959; Sherwood and Milby, 1961; Walter and Aitken, 1961; Donaldson and Millar, 1962; Balnave, 1969; Jackson, 1970), in some cases little difference in egg production has been reported (Combs, *et al.*, 1961; Balnave, 1970). Egg size is usually reduced by restricted feeding but the efficiency of conversion of ME to egg product is improved (Combs *et al.*, 1961; Jackson, 1970; Balnave, 1970).

From the evidence reviewed, it is apparent that for restricted feeding to be utilized satisfactorily during the laying period careful consideration must be given to accurate assessment of the mature body weight of the birds so that over-

24

restriction does not result in the birds being seriously underfed. It is apparent from most reports that feed restriction of 10% or more (compared with *ad libitum*) can seriously affect egg production, but there have recently been claims that much larger savings are possible (Petersen, 1971; Sykes, 1972).

FOWLS OF MEAT-PRODUCING STRAINS

Restriction during the rearing period

Pullets of the heavier stocks used for broiler production are not normally fed *ad libitum* during the growing stage, but are restricted in their feed intake so as to reduce liveweight, and particularly the amount of body fat, at the onset of egg production. There are very few published experiments relating to this practice, but there is no doubt from field experience that it is well justified. Not only is the cost of rearing reduced, but the subsequent reproductive performance of the flock is increased by ensuring that birds are not "over-weight" at point-of-lay. Unfortunately it is not possible to specify scales of feeding appropriate to stocks of different mature body sizes because the necessary data are lacking. However, it is usual for any breeding organisation which supplies broiler parent stock to recommend levels of feeding, and this is probably the best practice since the degree of restriction required may depend upon the particular genotype involved.

Restriction of breeding females

Restriction during the laying period was reported to increase egg production when birds were allowed 87·3% of the *ad libitum* intake but decrease it if the allowance was 81·6% (Singsen, Matterson, Tlustohowicz and Potter, 1959). Other authors (Pepper, Slinger, Summers and McConachie, 1966; Sherwood, Caskey, Krautmann, Van Wormer, Smith and Ward, 1964; Schumaier and McGinnis, 1969; Standlee, Strother, Creger and Couch, 1963) found that restriction reduced output.

Aitken, Meyer, Griesbach and Merritt (1963), and Standlee *et al.* (1963) reported that mortality was increased, whereas Pepper *et al.* (1966) found it was decreased, when the food was restricted.

Dymsza, Boucher and McCartney (1954), Parker and Arscott (1964) and Standlee *et al.* (1963) agreed that hatchability was decreased by restriction.

It is probable that the responses obtained are dependent on bird type and on the energy intakes allowed. Schumaier and McGinnis (1969) found that restriction during the laying period had no deleterious effects on egg production unless the birds had previously been fed *ad libitum*. It is therefore possible that birds accustomed to an *ad libitum* feeding régime do not react favourably to restricted feeding. There would appear to be little merit in restricting the feed of breeding females as a universal practice. However, restriction would be appropriate for any stock that showed evidence of excessive energy intakes on an *ad libitum* feeding system if the result was excessive fat deposition that was likely to have a deleterious effect on mortality and on mating behaviour.

Restriction of breeding males

Feed restriction of adult cocks appears to have no desirable effects on production. Undesirable effects of feed restriction during this period have been reported by Parker and Arscott (1964) who showed that a 32% loss of body weight in cocks was accompanied by a complete loss of fertility.

25

REFERENCES

AITKEN, J. R., MEYER, H. E. W., GRIESBACH, L. & MERRITT, E. S. (1963). *Can. J. Anim. Sci.* **43**, 290

ALLRED, J. B., FRY, R. E., JENSEN, L. S. & McGINNIS, J. (1957). *Poult. Sci.* **36**, 1284

ALLRED, J. B., JENSEN, L. S. & McGINNIS, J. (1957). *Poult. Sci.* **36**, 517

ANDREWS, L. D. & GOODWIN, T. L. (1969). *Poult. Sci.* **48**, 191

ARSCOTT, G. H., ROSE, R. J. & PARKER, J. E. (1962). *Oregon agric. exp. Stn Tech. Bull.* **64**

ATKINSON, R. L., KURNICK, A. A., FERGUSON, T. M., REID, B. L., QUISENBERRY, J. H. & COUCH, J. R. (1957). *Poult. Sci.* **36**, 767

AUCKLAND, J. N. & MORRIS, T. R. (1971). *Br. Poult. Sci.* **12**, 305

BALNAVE, D. (1969). *J. Sci. Fd Agric.* **20**, 556

BALNAVE, D. (1970). *Poult. Sci.* **49**, 1197

BALNAVE, D. (1971). *J. Sci. Fd Agric.* **22**, 125

BAROTT, H. G. & PRINGLE, E. M. (1946). *J. Nutr.* **31**, 35

BAYLEY, H. S., SUMMERS, J. D. & SLINGER, S. J. (1968). *Poult. Sci.* **47**, 1140

BELL, F. R. (1971). *Proc. Nutr. Soc.* **30**, 103

BIRD, S. & SINCLAIR, J. W. (1939). *Sci. Agric.* **19**, 542

BLACK, D. J. G., JENNINGS, R. C. & MORRIS, T. R. (1958). *Poult. Sci.* **37**, 707

BOLTON, W. (1958). *J. agric. Sci., Camb.* **50**, 97

BOLTON, W. (1959). *J. agric. Sci., Camb.* **52**, 364

BOORMAN, K. N. (1973). *Proc. Univ. Nottingham 7th Nutr, Conf. Fd Mfrs*, 107

BRODY, S., FUNK, E. M. & KEMPSTER, H. L. (1938). *Missouri agric. exp. Stn Res. Bull.* **278**

BROWN, W. O., WARING, J. J. & ADISSON, R. F. (1967). In *Progress in livestock nutrition 1962-1967*. US Feed Grains Council Publication

BURLACU, GH. & BALTAC, M. (1971). *J. agric. Sci., Camb.* **77**, 405

BURLACU, GH., BALTAC, M. & PARASCHIV, M. (1970). In *Energy metabolism of farm animals*. EAAP Publication No. 13. Ed. A. Schürch & C. Wenk. Zurich, Juris.

BURLACU, GH., GROSSU, D., MARINESCU, G., BALTAC, M. & GRUNCA, D. (1969). In *Energy metabolism of farm animals*. EAAP Publication No. 12. Ed. K. L. Blaxter J. Kielanowski & G. Thorbek. Newcastle, Oriel Press.

BYERLY, T. C. (1941. *Bull. Univ. Md agric. exp. Stn*, A1

CAREW, L. B. (1961). *Studies of the effects of dietary vegetable oils on growth rate, energy intake, tissue composition and energy metabolism of chicks*. Ph.D. Thesis, Cornell University.

CHARLES, D. R., PAYNE, C. G. & LAMMING, G. E. (1963). *Report Univ. Nottingham Sch. Agric.*, 93

COMBS, G. F. (1968). *Pac. S.W. Anim. Ind. Conf.*

COMBS, G. F., GATTIS, B. & SHAFFNER, C. S. (1961). *Poult Sci.* **40**, 220

CORNELL UNIVERSITY (1967). *Duck Rations*, Extension, Stencil No. 25

DAVIS, R. H., HASSAN. O. E. M. & SYKES, A. H. (1970). *Proc. Nutr. Soc.* **29**, 39A

DONALDSON, W. E. & MILLAR, R. I. (1962). *Poult. Sci.* **41**, 353

DYMSZA, H., BOUCHER, R. V. & McCARTNEY, M. G. (1954). *Poult. Sci.* **33**, 1159

EDWARDS, H. M. (1969). *Proc. Univ. Nottingham 3rd Nutr. Conf. Fd Mfrs*, 92

FOSTER, W. H. (1968). *Rec. agric. Res. Min. Agric. N. Ire.* **17**, 13

FULLER, H. L. & DUNAHOO, W. S. (1962). *Poult Sci.* **41**, 1306

GARDINER, E. E. & MACINTYRE, T. M. (1962). *Can. J. Anim. Sci.* **42**, 95

GELINEO, S. (1964). In *Handbook of Physiology*, Section 4 (pp. 259-282). Washington, American Physiological Society

GOSLING, J. M. (1970). *Nutritional and biochemical aspects of fat metabolism in chickens*. Ph.D. Thesis, Nottingham University.

GRIMBERGEN, A. H. M. (1970). *Neth. J. agric. Sci.* **18**, 195

HERVEY, G. R. (1971). *Proc. Nutr. Soc.* **30**, 109

HILL, F. W. (1962). In *Nutrition of pigs and poultry*. Ed. J. T. Morgan & D. Lewis. London, Butterworths.

HILL, F. W. (1969). *International encyclopaedia of food and nutrition.* **17**, 1137

HOWES, J. R., GRUB, W. & ROLLO, C. A. (1962). *Poult. Sci.* **41**, 1652

HUSTON, T. M. (1965). *Poult. Sci.* **44**, 1032

JACKSON, N. (1969). *42nd Ann. Rep. Agric. Res. Inst. N. Ire.*, 25

JACKSON, N. (1970). *Br. Poult, Sci.* **11,** 93
JACKSON, N., KIRKPATRICK, H. R. & FULTON, R. B. (1969). *Br. Poult, Sci.* **10,** 115
LEE, P. J. W. (1969a). *Restricted feeding of laying and breeding pullets during the rearing period.* Ph.D. Thesis, Univ. of Reading.
LEE, P. J. W., (1969b). *A consideration of energy levels for contrasting strains of commercial laying stock.* London, Vitamins Limited.
LEE, P. J. W., GULLIVER, A. L. & MORRIS, T. R. (1971). *Br. Poult, Sci.* **12,** 413.
LEESON, S. & PORTER-SMITH, A. J. (1970). *Br. Poult, Sci.* **11,** 275
LILLIE, R. J. & DENTON, C. A. (1966). *Poult. Sci.* **45,** 810
MacINTYRE, T. M. & GARDINER, E. E. (1964). *Poult. Sci.* **43,** 467
MacINTYRE, T. M. & JENKINS, M. H. (1955). *Poult. Sci.* **34,** 376
MAYER, J. & AREES, E. A. (1968). *Fedn Proc. Fedn Am. Socs exp. Biol.* **27,** 1345
MILBY, T. T. & SHERWOOD, D. H. (1956). *Poult. Sci.* **35,** 863
MILLIGAN, J. L. & WINN, P. N. (1964). *Poult. Sci.* **43,** 817
MORAN, E. T., SUMMERS, J. D. & ORR, H. L. (1969). *Br. Poult. Sci.* **10,** 127
MORRIS, T. R. (1967). In *Environmental control in poultry production.* Ed. T. C. Carter. Edinburgh, Oliver & Boyd.
MORRIS, T. R. (1968). *Br. Poult. Sci.* **9,** 285
MORRIS, T. R. (1969). *Proc. Univ. Nottingham 3rd Nutr. Conf. Fd Mfrs,* 103
MRAZ, F. R., BOUCHER, R. V. & McCARTNEY, M. G. (1956). *Poult. Sci.* **35,** 1335
MRAZ, F. R., BOUCHER, R. V. & McCARTNEY, M. G. (1957). *Poult. Sci.* **36,** 1217
MUELLER, W. J. (1961). *Poult. Sci.* **40,** 1562
O'NEILL, S. J. B. (1971). *Calorimetric studies on the effect of feathering and environmental temperature on heat production by the domestic fowl.* Ph.D. Thesis, Queen's University, Belfast
O'NEILL, S. J. B., BALNAVE, D. & JACKSON, N. (1971). *J. agric. Sci., Camb.* **77,** 293
OTA, H. (1960). *USDA Misc. Publ. 728,* Washington, D.C.
PARKER, J. E. & ARSCOTT, G. H. (1964). *J. Nutr.* **82,** 183
PAYNE, C. G. (1964). *Wld's Poult. Sci. Assoc., Report of 2nd European Conference, Bologna, Italy*
PAYNE, C. G. (1966). *Report of the Rural Electrification Conference, 1966.* p. 23. London, the Electricity Council.
PAYNE, C. G. (1967). In *Environmental control in poultry production.* Ed. T. C. Carter. Edinburgh, Oliver & Boyd
PEARCE, J. & BROWN, W. O. (1971). In *Physiology and biochemistry of the domestic fowl.* Ed. D. J. Bell & B. M. Freeman, London, Academic Press
PEPPER, W. F., SLINGER, S. J., SUMMERS, J. D. & McCONACHIE, J. D. (1966). *Poult. Sci.* **45,** 1397
PETERSEN, C. F. (1971). *Wld's Poult. Sci. J.* **27,** 161
PETERSEN, C. F., SAUTER, E. A., CONRAD, D. H. & LAMPMAN, C. E. (1960). *Poult. Sci.* **39,** 1010
POPE, D. L. (1960) *Proc. Md Nutr. Conf. Fd Mfrs,* 48
PORTER-SMITH, A. J. & SHRIMPTON, D. H. (1968). *Proc. Nutr. Soc.* **27,** 59A
PRINCE, R. P., POTTER, L. M. & IRISH, W. W. (1961). *Poult. Sci.* **40,** 102
PRINCE, R. P., WHITAKER, J. H., MATTERSON, L. D. & LUGINBUHL, R. E. (1965). *Poult. Sci.* **44,** 73
ROMIJN, C. & VREUGDENHIL, E. L. (1969). *Neth. J. vet. Sci.* **2,** 32
ROMOSER, G. L. & HELBACKA, N. V. (1958). *Proc. Md Nutr. Conf. Fd Mfrs,* 55
SCHUMAIER, G. & McGINNIS, J. (1969). *Poult. Sci.* **48,** 949
SHANNON, D. W. F. (1966). *Respiration calorimetric studies on dietary and environmental factors influencing the utilization of energy in the common fowl.* Ph. D. Thesis, Queen's University, Belfast
SHANNON, D. W. F. & BROWN, W. O. (1969a). *J. agric. Sci., Camb.* **72,** 479
SHANNON, D. W. F. & BROWN, W. O. (1969b). *Br. Poult. Sci.* **10,** 13
SHANNON, D. W. F. & BROWN, W. O. (1970). *Br. Poult, Sci.* **11,** 1
SHANNON, D. W. F., WARING, J. J. & BROWN, W. O. (1969). In *Energy metabolism of farm animals.* EAAP Publication No. 12. Ed. K. L. Blaxter, J. Kielanowski & G. Thorbek. Newcastle, Oriel Press
SHERWOOD, D. H. (1959). *Poult. Sci.* **38,** 1246
SHERWOOD, D. H., CASKEY, C. D., KRAUTMANN, B. A., VAN WORMER, M. C., SMITH, S. B. & WARD, R. E. (1964). *Poult. Sci.* **43,** 1272

27

SHERWOOD, D. E. & MILBY, T. T. (1961). *Poult. Sci.* **40**, 80
SIBBALD, I. R., SLINGER, S. J. & ASHTON, G. C. (1960). *J. Nutr.* **72**, 441
SINGSEN, E. P., MATTERSON, L. D., TLUSTOHOWICZ, J. & POTTER, L. M. (1959). *Storrs agric. exp. Stn Bull.* 346
SMITH, A. J. (1971). *Feedstuffs, Minneap.* **43**, (17), 26
SMITH, J. H. (1967). *Poult. Sci.* **46**, 1320
SNYDER, E. S. (1959). *Duck and Goose Raising*, Ontario Dept Agric. Publ. 532.
STANDLEE, W. J., STROTHER, A., CREGER, C. R. & COUCH, J. R. (1963). *Poult. Sci.* **42**, 452
SUMMERS, J. D., PEPPER, W. F., MORAN, E. T. & McCONACHIE, J. D. (1968). *Poult. Sci.* **47**, 536
SYKES, A. H. (1972). In *Egg formation and production*. Ed. B. M. Freeman & P. E. Lake. Edinburgh, Constable
TITUS, H. W. (1928). *Poult. Sci.* **8**, 80
VAN ES., A. J. H., VIK-MO, L., JANSSEN, H., BOSCH, A., SPREEUWENBERG, W., VOGT, J. E. & NIJKAMP, H. J. (1970). In *Energy metabolism of farm animals*. EAAP Publication No. 13. Ed. A. Schürch & C. Wenk. Zurich, Juris.
VAN KAMPEN, M. & ROMIJN, C. (1970). In *Energy metabolism of farm animals*. EAAP Publication No. 13. Ed. A. Schürch & C. Wenk. Zurich, Juris.
VOHRA, P. (1967). *Wld's Poult. Sci. J.*
WALTER, E. D. & AITKEN, J. R. (1961). *Poult. Sci.* **40**, 345
WARING, J. J., ADDISON, R. F. & BROWN, W. O. (1968). *Br. Poult. Sci.* **9**, 79
WARING, J. J. & BROWN, W. O. (1965). *J. agric. Sci., Camb.* **65**, 139
WARING, J. J. & BROWN, W. O. (1967). *J. agric. Sci., Camb.* **68**, 149
WELLS, R. G. (1967). Report R/1, BEMB Poultry Husbandry Experimental Unit, Edgmond, Shropshire
WELLS, R. G. (1969a), Report R/6, BEMB Poultry Husbandry Experimental Unit. Edgmond, Shropshire
WELLS, R. G. (1969b), Report R/7, BEMB Poultry Husbandry Experimental Unit, Edgmond, Shropshire

CHAPTER 2

REQUIREMENTS FOR PROTEIN

The synthesis of protein in animal tissues requires an adequate supply of about twenty different amino acids. Some of these cannot be synthesised by the animal and must therefore be provided in the diet; such amino acids are termed essential or indispensable. Of the remaining amino acids some are readily synthesised in the body and are termed non-essential or dispensable. Others are not so easily classified, either because they can only be formed by the animal from essential amino acids, or because the rate at which they are formed from simple precursors is not always sufficient to meet the demands of productive processes.

Table 2.1

Nutritional classification of the amino acids

Lysine	⎤	Tyrosine	{ can be formed from phenylalanine
Methionine			
Threonine		Cystine	{ can be formed from methionine
Tryptophan		Glycine	⎫ interconvertible
Isoleucine		Serine	⎬ but synthesis is sometimes inadequate
Leucine	⎬ essential	Proline	{ synthesis sometimes inadequate
Valine			
Phenylalanine		Alanine	⎫
Histidine		Aspartic Acid	⎬ non-essential
Arginine	⎦	Glutamic Acid	⎭

For the fowl (and probably for other poultry also) ten amino acids (listed in Table 2.1) are essential. Each of these amino acids must be provided in the diet in accordance with the requirements established for particular productive processes. It is generally accepted that alanine, aspartic acid and glutamic acid are readily formed in the tissues of the fowl, provided that a diet adequate in energy and overall protein content is fed. These amino acids are, therefore, non-essential and their proportions in diets containing commonly-used ingredients are not critical. Some experimental diets involve the use of mixtures of purified amino acids in place of intact protein and in such diets the use of a high level of a single non-essential amino acid may impair performance. In this type of diet a mixture of non-essential amino acids is preferable to reliance on a single source.

The amino acids tyrosine and cystine (or cysteine, which is the metabolically active form of cystine) can be formed in the tissues; but because they are formed from the essential amino acids phenylalanine and methionine respectively they are usually considered in conjunction with those amino acids. Thus a dietary requirement for phenylalanine + tyrosine is recognised, as well as a specific requirement for phenylalanine, and a deficiency of tyrosine can be compensated for by an increase in the phenylalanine content of the diet. Tyrosine cannot be converted to phenylalanine in the animal and thus a definite proportion

29

(approximately 50%) of the combined requirement must be provided as phenylalanine. A similar situation obtains for methionine and cystine, a methionine + cystine requirement being recognised, approximately 60% of which must be provided as methionine. The possibility that some cystine is formed from precursors other than methionine in the tissues of the fowl cannot be ignored, but for practical purposes it is advisable, at present, to continue to regard methionine as the sole precursor of cystine.

Although glycine càn be synthesised in tissues, it is thought that the rate of synthesis of this amino acid is not sufficiently rapid to meet the demands of high levels of production (Almquist and Grau, 1944). It has been the practice, therefore, to ensure that the supply of glycine in the diet is adequate. Recently, however, it has become apparent that the glycine requirement cannot be considered in isolation from the serine content of the diet. Glycine and serine are interconvertible in animal tissues and available information suggests that formation from serine represents the most important pathway for glycine synthesis in birds. It therefore appears that the limiting factor in glycine synthesis is the rate of formation of serine from carbohydrate precursors and that a glycine + serine requirement, which can be satisfied by increasing the dietary level of either amino acid, should be recognised (Akrabawi and Kratzer, 1968).

In some experimental diets a need for proline has been demonstrated (Graber, Allen and Scott, 1970). In mammals this amino acid is formed from glutamic acid, and the chick apparently has a limited ability to effect this conversion (Bhargava, Shen, Bird and Sunde, 1971). Proline formation from the essential amino acid arginine has been observed in the fowl (Klain and Johnson, 1962) but the quantitative significance of this conversion remains to be established. Although it is very unlikely that proline will be limiting in practical diets, it is advisable to ensure an adequate level of proline in diets based on free amino acids or unusual protein sources.

Definition of a protein requirement

The protein "requirement" of an animal is really a requirement for a supply of each of the essential amino acids, together with a sufficient supply of suitable nitrogenous compounds from which the non-essential amino acids can be synthesised. It is unsatisfactory to specify a protein requirement as a single figure, since the amount of protein which must be supplied depends upon the yields of amino acids obtained by the animal when that protein is digested. Nor is it feasible to identify the "quality" of a protein (i.e. its value to the animal as compared with alternative dietary proteins) in the form of a single numerical value, because firstly, such values cannot be made additive, secondly they cannot apply to several different physiological circumstances and thirdly, their use in the formulation of diets inevitably leads to an inefficient use of protein. The quality of a protein can only be usefully described in terms of the amino acids which it supplies to the animal. It is, however, useful to specify a total requirement for crude protein, in addition to specifying requirements for each of the essential amino acids, since this conveniently ensures that the diet supplies sufficient precursors for the synthesis of the non-essential amino acids. An alternative is to specify the requirements for non-essential amino acids as a proportion of the total requirement for essential amino acids.

The remainder of this Chapter will be mainly concerned with estimates of requirements for essential amino acids. Earlier experimental work dealing with estimates of "protein requirement" is not reviewed, since the amino acid content of the diets used in those trials is largely unknown and no evidence is available to show which amino acid was limiting performance.

Factors affecting amino acid requirements

Increasing recognition is given to the fact that absolute levels of amino acids within a diet should not be defined in isolation from other nutrients. Supply within a unit of time is substantially influenced by the overall rate of feed intake which is in turn regulated to a considerable extent by the concentration of energy-yielding nutrients in the diet. It is therefore desirable either to define amino acid supply relative to a particular nutrient, whether it be the level of a certain amino acid, of protein or of dietary energy, or to deal directly with daily intakes of amino acids.

Since amino acids in general enter into a variety of metabolic pathways it has been widely assumed that any surplus ingested and not subsequently used for protein synthesis exerts no adverse effects. It should be recognised, however, that surpluses of amino acids necessarily reduce the efficiency of utilization of the total protein content of a diet, the magnitude of this effect depending upon the extent of the deviation from an ideal balance of amino acids. There are, moreover, certain instances in which a dietary excess of an amino acid, or of a mixture of amino acids, is known to precipitate an ill-effect which is totally disproportionate to the degree of imbalance (Harper, Benevenga and Wohlhueter, 1970). Following the consumption of such an imbalanced diet there are reductions both in the rate of growth and in feed intake. There has been some controversy as to which of these features is the primary consequence of the consumption of the imbalanced diet but convincing information is now available showing a marked depression in feed intake after 3 to 6 hours. This implies that the depression in feed intake is the primary effect, which in turn is responsible for the retardation in growth (Harper and Rogers, 1965; D'Mello and Lewis, 1971).

It is thus not invariably adequate to specify minimum levels of essential amino acids in the diet. The growth retardation which may be encountered as a result of the presence of an excess of a particular amino acid, or an overall imbalance, can generally be prevented by including in the diet quantities of another amino acid greater than the amount normally considered as the requirement. It can therefore be said that, in these cases, the effect of including an excess of one amino acid is to increase the apparent requirement for another. Such an inter-relationship can be built into a concept of inter-dependence in requirements between two amino acids, or groups of amino acids (D'Mello and Lewis, 1970). Balance would then be achieved by specifying minimum quantities of all essential amino acids as a function of one particular amino acid, and by ensuring that the inter-dependent amino acids (lysine and arginine; tryptophan and threonine; leucine, valine and isoleucine) were kept in an appropriate ratio, one to the other.

Although an amino acid imbalance can produce dramatic results under certain experimental conditions, it is doubtful whether similar problems arise from the surpluses of essential amino acids likely to be derived from the digestion of practical diets. The available evidence suggests that moderate surpluses of essential amino acids, supplied as intact proteins, can be ignored in routine formulation. However, an excess of an individual amino acid may occur in a practical diet if free amino acids (such as methionine and lysine) are added without due regard for the requirement of the animal, and this can have serious consequences.

Methods of assessing essential amino acid requirements

To ensure an adequate supply of essential amino acids to the animal it is necessary to obtain estimates of: (i) the quantitative requirements of the animal for each amino acid, (ii) the concentrations of amino acids in the various feedingstuffs to be used, and (iii) the extent to which the amino acids in the intact proteins of the feed are available to the animal.

The data which have been used in estimating requirements for essential amino acids were derived from feeding trials in which growth rate, feed conversion efficiency or egg output have been the parameters of response. Although the efficiency of utilization of an essential amino acid in a low-protein diet can be very high (Morris, 1972) there is not sufficient evidence about rates of utilization with diets which are adequate for maximum performance. It is therefore not possible to calculate amino acid requirements from a theoretical consideration of the rates at which amino acids are used for different processes within the animal; but it is sometimes possible to derive estimates from the empirical data available, enabling appropriate adjustments to be made to requirements for differences in growth rate, body size or egg output.

Data for the total amino acid content of feedingstuffs are accumulating (Harvey, 1970; FAO, 1970), but these amino acids may not be completely available for a number of reasons. The physical nature of the feedingstuff, the physico-chemical nature of the protein, and the extent of chemical interactions between the amino acids and carbohydrates in the feedingstuff can all affect availability. These characteristics can be modified both advantageously and adversely by the processing of the feedingstuff. The standard method of measuring availability is by biological assay, using either growth rate or the feed conversion efficiency of chicks. The time, cost and variability involved in such assays preclude their routine use and so microbiological and chemical methods have been sought which provide effective substitutes. Of these latter methods, only the chemical estimation of available lysine, originally developed by Carpenter, Ellinger, Munro and Rolfe (1957), has found consistent use. The problem of providing reliable routine estimates of amino acid availability for specific batches of ingredients therefore remains largely unsolved. As data on availabilities accumulate however it may be possible to provide typical availability values for each type of feedingstuff so that due allowance can be made for this factor in the formulation of diets.

Not all of the published experimental data have been found suitable for inclusion in this review. Estimates of requirement are usually made by adding graded doses of one amino acid to a basal diet supposed to be adequate in all other amino acids and all other nutrients. This technique is satisfactory so long as the evidence shows that the basal diet does not support normal performance, and so long as a level of performance comparable with the best contemporary practical diets can be achieved by the simple addition of the limiting amino acid. In many cases the highest output achieved has fallen short of this standard and this means that the estimate of requirement obtained is likely to be too low.

AMINO ACID REQUIREMENTS OF GROWING POULTRY

The procedure of identifying requirements for each of the essential amino acids in turn suffers from the difficulty that the requirement for one animo acid estimated in a particular experiment may be affected by the levels selected for all the other amino acids in that experiment. It has therefore been decided to deal first with the question of an optimum pattern of amino acids (i.e. to deal with *relative* concentrations in the diet), leaving the question of the absolute concentrations of amino acids to be discussed later. The following section refers to data obtained with young growing chicks, but we assume, for the want of any better information, that the "optimal pattern" of amino acids which is selected can be applied in the formulation of diets for other classes of rapidly growing poultry.

An attempt has been made to identify for the young chick a pattern or balance of amino acids which will support maximum growth and feed conversion efficiency. A selection of some published sets of data is given in Table 2.2. These include the previous recommendations of the Agricultural Research Council (1963) and the latest recommendations of the National Research Council of the U.S.A. A set of "selected values" has been prepared from an examination of all the evidence and is given in the final column of Table 2.2.

The results obtained in one set of experiments, such as those of Dobson, Anderson and Warnick (1964) or Dean and Scott (1965), define levels of amino acids which supported maximum performance but do not preclude the possibility that lower levels of some amino acids might have given equally good results. The figures therefore represent upper limits to the estimates of requirement, rather than final minimum values.

AMINO ACID REQUIREMENTS OF THE CHICK

Chicks from 0 to 4 weeks of age

Given that the selected values shown in Table 2.2 represent an optimal balance of essential amino acids, the optimal dietary concentration for all amino acids can, in principle, be determined by estimating the requirements for any one of them. Since lysine is commonly the first limiting amino acid in chick diets, and there is more evidence available for lysine than for any other amino acid, the requirement for lysine has been estimated from a survey of published experiments.

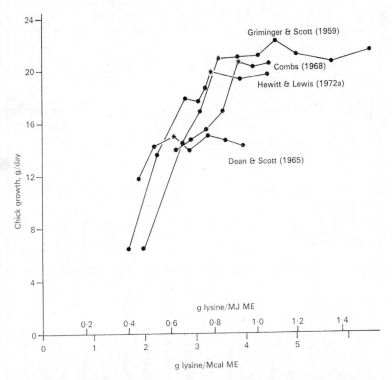

Fig. 2.1. Growth response to dietary lysine in four selected trials. The asterisks mark the points chosen as representing the "requirement" in each of these four experiments.

33

Table 2.2
Amino acid requirements of the young chick (g amino acid/kg diet) as recommended by various authorities

	Agricultural Research Council (1963)	Dobson, Anderson & Warnick (1964)	Dean & Scott (1965)	Zimmerman & Scott (1965)	Hewitt (1968)	National Research Council (1971)	Preferred* estimate g/kg	Preferred* estimate relative to lysine = 100
Lysine	10·0	11·5	11·2	9·5	8·5	12·5	9·0	100
Arginine	—	12·8	11·0	10·0	8·5	14·0	8·5	94
Histidine	3·5	4·3	3·0	3·0	4·0	4·6	4·0	44
Tryptophan	1·5	2·0	2·25	1·5	1·7	2·3	1·7	19
Threonine	5·5	7·8	6·5	6·5	5·3	8·0	6·0	67
Phenylalanine	6·0	6·7	6·8	5·0	7·2	8·0	7·0	78
Phenylalanine + Tyrosine	12·0	13·3	13·1	9·5	15·7	15·0	13·0	144
Methionine	2·8	4·0	4·5	3·5	3·9	4·6	4·0	44
Methionine + Cystine	7·0	7·3	8·0	7·0	7·9	8·6	7·5	83
Leucine	15·0	13·0	12·0	12·0	13·4	16·0	12·0	133
Isoleucine	5·0	8·0	8·0	8·0	6·1	8·6	7·0	78
Valine	8·0	9·5	8·2	8·2	7·9	10·0	8·0	89
Glycine	10·0	—	16·0	12·0	6·1	10·0	—	—
Glycine + Serine	—	—	—	—	11·3	11·5	11·4	127

* These values indicate relative rather than absolute requirements; see Table 2.4.

34

Nine reports were found giving results of experiments in which graded doses of lysine had been fed to chicks, with a sufficient range of doses to indicate where the requirement lay. Figure 2.1 illustrates the general character of the responses obtained in four of the experiments and Table 2.3 lists all of the sources used in arriving at an estimate of requirement. The values given in the last column of Table 2.3 are subjective estimates obtained by choosing the lowest level of dietary lysine which gave maximum, or near-maximum, growth. Some of the difficulties of making this judgement are illustrated in Figure 2.1. There is no apparent relationship between the estimated requirement in any one trial and the maximum growth rate reached in that trial. This implies that faster growing chickens do not need a higher concentration of lysine (relative to energy) in their diet than slow-growing chickens, which accords with the conclusions of Griminger and Scott (1959). Faster growing chickens do, of course, need a greater daily intake of lysine than slow-growing strains, but they achieve this higher intake because, to satisfy their requirements for energy, they consume more feed.

Table 2.3
Sources used to estimate the lysine requirement of the chick from 0 to 4 weeks of age

Source	Experiment no.	Duration days of age	Maximum growth rate g/d	Dietary energy Mcal ME/kg	Lysine level giving maximum (or near maximum) growth g lysine/Mcal ME
Bornstein (1970)	2	1–36	16·5	2·92	3·01*
Combs (1968)	CP58	1–29	21·0	3·36	3·84*
Edwards et al. (1956)	1	1–29	5·0	3·29	2·74
Dean & Scott (1965)	12	8–14	15·0	4·36	2·57*
Griminger & Scott (1959)	1	13–27	18·5	2·67	3·86*
	1	13–27	16·0	2·67	3·86*
	2	13–27	21·0	2·67	3·48*
	2	13–27	13·5	2·67	3·48
	2	13–27	10·5	2·67	3·48
	3	7–28	17·0	2·62	4·23*
	3	7–28	13·5	2·62	4·23
Hewitt & Lewis (1972a) (1972b)	3	7–21	15·0	3·42	2·06
	3	7–21	20·0	3·14	3·35*
	4	7–21	18·0	3·38	2·32
Schwartz et al. (1958)	3	1–26	12·0	2·42	4·13
	3	1–26	13·5	2·86	4·20
	3	1–26	14·5	3·29	3·95
Uwaegbute & Lewis (1966)	1	7–21	16·5	2·79	3·26*
	6	7–21	20·0	3·06	4·01*
Zimmerman & Scott (1965)	1	8–15	13·5	4·37	2·06

* Selected values used in arriving at an estimate of mean requirement (see text).

Nevertheless, in estimating the requirement for present-day broiler chickens we have chosen to exclude trials in which maximum growth rate was less than 15 g/d. We have also excluded experiment 4 of Hewitt and Lewis (1972b) because the total protein level was rather low in this trial. This leaves ten trials, marked with an asterisk in Table 2.3, which lead to an estimated average lysine requirement of chicks from 0 to 4 weeks of age of 3·55 g/Mcal ME (0·85 g/MJ).

Although there is little doubt that a lysine concentration of 3·55 g/Mcal ME, in association with the amino acid balance given in Table 2.2, will give "maximum or near maximum" early chick growth, the use of a single estimate of requirement is unsatisfactory. The variation in values in the last column of Table 2.3 represents not so much variation due to different stocks or diets or environments, but uncertainty in determining an end point on a continuous curve. Clearly what is needed is a curve which will define the expected rate of response in liveweight gain for each increment of lysine. It has not proved possible to derive satisfactory curves from published data.

One other feature of the data in Table 2.3 deserves comment. There is a tendency for experiments in which high dietary energy levels were used to give low estimates of requirement (expressed as g lysine/Mcal ME). This raises the question whether the expression of "lysine requirement" as a function of dietary energy is satisfactory. However, if the lysine requirement is expressed as g lysine/kg of diet there is then a positive correlation between the requirement and dietary energy. Presumably, in those experiments in which very high energy diets were used there was a greater deposition of fat in the carcase and, for this reason, the optimum ratio of lysine to energy in the diet was smaller.

For other amino acids the body of evidence available is much smaller than for lysine. It is recommended that minimal standards for the remaining essential amino acids should be set in relation to the selected lysine requirement, using the optimal amino acid pattern given in the last column of Table 2.2.

Chickens from 4 to 8 weeks of age

For the 4 to 8 week stage of growth, the only published results which provide a basis for estimating requirement appear to be those of Combs (1968). In two trials in which maximum growth rates of almost 40 g/d were reached, the apparent lysine requirements were 2·44 and 2·66 g/Mcal (0·583 and 0·636 g/MJ). The average value, 2·55 g lysine/Mcal ME (0·610 g/MJ), has therefore been adopted as an estimate of requirement for this stage of growth.

Table 2.4

Estimated dietary lysine* requirement for maximum chick growth, using diets of different metabolizable energy content

Dietary ME		Lysine requirement, g/kg diet	
Mcal/kg	MJ/kg	0–4 weeks	4–8 weeks
2·6	11·0	9·2	6·6
3·0	12·5	10·7	7·6
3·4	14·0	12·1	8·6

* Estimates of requirements for other amino acids can be obtained by using these values for lysine together with the ratios given in the last column of Table 2.2 (see also Table 6.1).

Table 2.4 gives estimates of lysine requirement as a proportion of the diet for various levels of dietary ME.

36

The total concentration of dietary essential amino acids represented by the different authorities listed in Table 2.2 ranges from 87 g/kg (Zimmerman and Scott, 1965) to 112 g/kg (NRC, 1971). These different estimates correspond to crude protein levels in practical diets of about 180 g/kg and 230 g/kg respectively. It is likely that the need for nitrogen to support the synthesis of non-essential amino acids will be adequately met by protein levels in this range. When diets are formulated from natural feedstuffs, it is usually sufficient to specify minimum levels for each of the essential amino acids without consideration of the need for non-essential nitrogen (Blair, 1972). However, the use of very low protein cereals or cereal substitutes, the inclusion of unusual protein sources or reliance on substantial amounts of synthetic amino acids could lead to the formulation of diets in which the supply of non-essential amino nitrogen was limiting. When semi-purified diets are being constructed for laboratory use, a minimum content of 30 g N/kg (equivalent to 188 g crude protein/kg) will ensure that no deficiency of non-essential nitrogen arises. The true requirement may well be less than this.

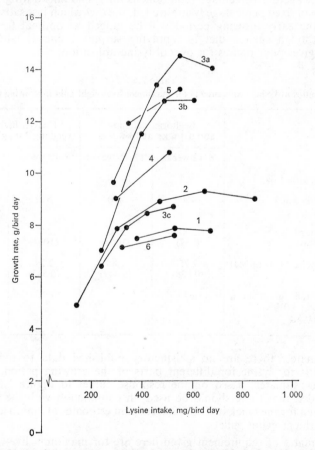

Fig. 2.2. The relation between average growth rate of pullets from 8 to 18 weeks of age and the calculated average daily intake of lysine. Key to sources: 1—Berg (1959); 2—Waldroup & Harms (1962); 3a, b, c—University of Reading (unreported experiment, in which lysine was shown to be the limiting amino acid); 4—Lillie & Denton (1967); 5—Summers *et al.* (1967); 6—Lillie & Denton (1966).

Very little direct evidence is available concerning the amino acid requirements of pullets between 8 and 20 weeks of age. Lee, Gulliver and Morris (1971a) have reviewed a number of experiments in which lysine was probably the factor limiting growth and were able to show a reasonably consistent set of relationships between calculated lysine intakes and daily liveweight gain (see Figure 2.2). From this information the average lysine requirement for maximum growth between 8 and 20 weeks is estimated as about 550 mg/day for the heavier type of laying pullet growing at an average rate of 12 to 14 g/day, and about 450 mg lysine/day for the smallest types of pullet which grow at a rate of 7 to 8 g/day.

When these figures are compared with the estimates made for young chicks they seem rather high, implying that the net efficiency of lysine utilization has declined with age. However, a more likely explanation is that the data are misleading to the extent that, in all these experiments, the same diet was fed from 8 through to 20 weeks. Because feed intake increases markedly between 8 and 12 weeks of age the percentage requirement for lysine falls during this period. When diets of fixed percentage lysine are fed, the diet which just satisfies requirements in the early growing period will be judged as optimal for the whole period, although such a diet is supplying surplus lysine at later ages and inevitably gives poor figures for overall lysine utilization.

Table 2.5

Estimates of lysine requirements for maximum liveweight gain in growing pullets

	Leghorns weighing about 1·6 kg at 18 weeks		Heavier laying strains weighing 2·0 kg at 18 weeks	
	8–12 weeks	12–18 weeks	8–12 weeks	12–18 weeks
Growth rate, g/bird day	8	8	14	14
Lysine requirement mg/bird day	450	450	550	550
Feed intake/bird day kcal ME (kJ ME)	200 (837)	240 (1004)	240 (1004)	280 (1172)
Dietary lysine, g/Mcal (g/MJ)	2·25 (0·538)	1·88 (0·449)	2·29 (0·547)	1·95 (0·466)
Lysine required (g/kg) in a diet containing 3·0 Mcal (12·6 MJ) ME/kg	6·7	5·6	6·9	5·9

Unfortunately there are no satisfactory published data to indicate exact requirements for lysine for different parts of the growing period. Table 2.5 gives some estimates, based on the response curves in Figure 2.2, and it is recommended that these should be used, in conjunction with the amino acid pattern given for the chick in Table 2.2, to form estimates of amino acid requirements for the growing pullet.

The estimates of requirement given here are for maximum live-weight gain. It may be that this is not always an appropriate objective in rearing pullets as it has been argued that the use of low-protein rearing diets will both save costs and lead to pullets which give better performances when in lay. This subject has been reviewed by Lee, Gulliver and Morris (1971a). The practice of feeding low protein diets to growing pullets has not been generally adopted and the advantages seem to be marginal for pullets of egg-producing strains. For broiler-breeding pullets, restriction of energy intake seems a more satisfactory procedure than the *ad libitum* feeding of a low protein diet (Lee, Gulliver and Morris, 1971b).

AMINO ACID REQUIREMENTS OF TURKEYS

It is difficult to establish amino acid requirements for turkeys by identifying, as for growing chicks, a dietary pattern which represents good balance. Such an approach does not seem to have been adopted in any published experimental programme; nor has it been possible to extract from published information adequate data relating intakes of an amino acid (e.g. lysine) to liveweight gain such that a satisfactory relationship can be established. Experiments ostensibly designed to assess lysine requirements have been simple supplementation studies and have not used basal diets which were demonstrably deficient in lysine and adequate in other respects. In some instances multiple supple-

Table 2.6
Amino acid requirements of turkey poults (0-8 weeks of age), assuming a diet containing 280 g crude protein/kg and about 3 Mcal ME/kg (12·6 MJ ME/kg)

	Median estimates derived from the literature		Preferred estimate	
	Sources	Requirement, g/kg	g/kg	relative to lysine = 100
Lysine	2, 3, 11	15·1	13	100
Arginine	2	15·7	12	92
Histidine	5	9·9	5	38
Tryptophan	4, 9	2·7	2·2	17
Threonine	—		9	69
Phenylalanine	5, 12	5·0	8	62
Phenylalanine + tyrosine	—		14	108
Methionine	1, 2, 6, 8, 11, 13	5·1	5	38
Methionine + cystine	2, 6, 8, 13	8·1	8	62
Leucine	—		14	108
Isoleucine	10	8·0	9	69
Valine	12	8·6	10	77
Glycine + serine	7	9·0	9	69

Key to sources

1. Baldini *et al.* (1957)
2. Balloun (1962)
3. Balloun & Phillips (1957)
4. Bird (1950)
5. Dunkelgod (1968)
6. Fitzsimmons & Waibel (1962)
7. Kratzer & Williams (1948)

8. Kratzer *et al.* (1949)
9. Kratzer *et al.* (1951)
10. Kratzer *et al.* (1952)
11. Sherman *et al.* (1960)
12. Snetsinger *et al.* (1964)
13. Waibel (1959)

mentation of amino acids led to difficulties in interpretation whilst in other cases the growth data were not adequately supported by information on food intake or efficiency of food utilization.

It, therefore, seems inevitable that amino acid requirements for turkeys must be extrapolated from other avian species or considered for single amino acids in isolation where some observations are available. The lysine and methionine requirements have been determined by several groups of workers; single estimates are available for some other amino acids whilst for others there seems to be no published requirement value based upon experimental results. A series of recommendations is given in Tables 2.6 and 2.7 based upon the published information indicated and in some instances upon an examination of chick values, turkey carcass composition or levels known to support satisfactory growth with conventional diets. Such an approach has been reviewed by Snetsinger (1967).

Table 2.7
Lysine and methionine requirements of older growing turkeys (no data available for other amino acids). The values are expressed as g/kg of diet, assuming an energy content of about 2·95 Mcal ME/kg (12·3 MJ ME/kg)

	Age in weeks		
	8–12	12–18	18–24
Lysine	10·4	9·3	8·8
Methionine	3·8	3·6	3·4
Methionine + cystine	6·4	5·7	5·1
Protein	220	190	160

The values given in Table 2.7 for lysine or methionine together with the ratio given in Table 2.6 can be used to estimate requirements for amino acids other than lysine and methionine for older growing turkeys.

The protein and amino acid requirements of breeding turkeys have not been investigated to any appreciable extent. Although levels of protein as low as 120 g/kg have been found to be satisfactory the usual recommended value is around 150 g/kg of diet. It can only be assumed that a pattern of amino acid balance similar to that proposed for the growing turkey be adopted. There is very little published information available on the amino acid requirements of turkeys based upon experimental work carried out in the United Kingdom.

AMINO ACID REQUIREMENTS OF DUCKLINGS

Information concerning the amino acid requirements of ducklings is very limited. There has been only one published report of an experiment which was specifically designed to determine an amino acid requirement (Dean, 1967a). In view of the lack of published information it is necessary to estimate the amino acid requirements for ducklings using the established amino acid requirements of the chick (see Table 2.2). Dean (1967a) used a basal diet composed of maize starch, isolated soyabean protein, maize oil and a mineral and vitamin supplement. The ration had a calculated energy value of 3·90 Mcal (16·3 MJ) ME/kg, and a crude protein content of 270 g/kg. Dean fed this diet with supplements of 0, 1, 2, 3 or 4 g/kg of DL-methionine to ducklings from 0–10 days of age. From

40

the results obtained it would appear that the ducklings required no more than 7·4 g methionine + cystine/kg. If one assumes that the relationship between amino acid requirements is the same for both young chicks and ducklings, then it is possible to estimate the requirements for the other essential amino acid requirements of ducklings (Table 2.8). It must be emphasised that these requirements are estimated values for ducklings between 0 and 10 days of age.

Table 2.8

Amino acid requirements of ducklings, based on the estimated methionine plus cystine requirement of Dean (1967a) and the chick amino acid pattern given in Table 2.2. These estimates relate to a diet with a calculated energy content of 3·9 Mcal (16·3 MJ) ME/kg

	Estimated requirement, g/kg
Lysine	8·9
Arginine	8·4
Histidine	3·9
Tryptophan	1·7
Threonine	5·9
Phenylalanine + tyrosine	12·8
Methionine + cystine	7·4
Leucine	11·8
Isoleucine	6·9
Valine	7·9
Glycine + serine	11·3

In addition to this one study there have been several reported experiments designed to determine the protein requirements of ducklings (Scott, Hill, Parsons, Bruckner and Dougherty, 1959; Dean, 1967b). Scott *et al.* (1959) showed that the protein : energy ratio of the diet had a very significant effect on the fat content of the carcass. With small protein : energy ratios there were excessive amounts of fat in the carcass and when the ratio was increased the fat content was reduced. They recommended that the diet fed to ducks from 0 to 49 days should have a protein : energy ratio of about 65 g/Mcal (16 g/MJ) with a minimum energy level of 2·75 Mcal (11·5 MJ) ME/kg. In more recent studies, Dean (1967b) has determined the "protein" requirements for ducklings at different ages. He reported that a protein : energy ratio of 74 g/Mcal (18 g/MJ) was optimum from 0 to 14 days. During the third week the optimum ratio was 66 g/Mcal (16 g/MJ), in the fourth week 58 g/Mcal (14 g/MJ) and after the fourth week it was 51 g/Mcal (12 g/MJ).

AMINO ACID REQUIREMENTS OF GEESE

Very little work has been carried out on the amino acid or protein requirements of geese. Most of the work reported has been carried out in the hot arid areas of the United States. Robertson and Francis (1966) determined the lysine requirement of young White Chinese goslings and concluded that it was about 9 g/kg in a diet containing 2·65 to 2·73 Mcal ME/kg (11·1 to 11·4 MJ/kg). The remaining amino acid requirements can only be estimated using chick requirement values.

AMINO ACID REQUIREMENTS OF ADULT FOWLS

The amino acids which are indispensable for adult fowls are the same as those listed for the chick (see Table 2.1), except that glycine is totally dispensable from laying diets.

The effects of surpluses of some amino acids on the estimate of requirements for others seems to be less of a problem with adults than with rapidly growing chicks. In practical diets there is probably no need to guard against surpluses of essential amino acids supplied by intact proteins. Free amino acids should only be added in amounts calculated to meet the requirement, since an excess of lysine or methionine may depress performance.

MAINTENANCE REQUIREMENTS

The maintenance requirements of a hen are difficult to estimate, since if she is not laying eggs she is likely to be either moulting or broody and hence not physiologically comparable with the normal laying fowl. Estimates of the maintenance requirements of the cock have been made and these are given in Table 2.9. The same values are probably applicable to the hen.

Table 2·9
Estimates of the amino acid requirements for maintenance in the adult fowl (assuming complete availability of dietary amino acids)

| | Requirement for positive nitrogen balance in the cock, mg/kg day | | Preferred estimate for hens and cocks |
	Leveille & Fisher (1959, 1960) and Leveille, Shapiro & Fisher (1960)	Kandatsu & Ishibashi (1966)	mg/kg day
Lysine	29	60	60
Arginine	120	32	40
Histidine	0	10	10
Tryptophan	19	10	10
Threonine	74	20	20
Phenylalanine	26	0	10
Phenylalanine + Tyrosine	60	20	30
Methionine	71	25	40
Methionine + Cystine	90	50	60
Leucine	124	20	40
Isoleucine	72	40	40
Valine	61	40	40

The total daily requirement of an adult cock for essential amino acids is about 300 mg/kg live-weight. Thus the needs of a 5 kg male would be met by about 4 g/day of feed protein and it is clear that any diet based on cereals will supply more than enough protein for the adult cock.

LAYING HENS

Although it is possible to maintain laying hens on synthetic diets with all the amino acids supplied in crystalline form (Johnson and Fisher, 1958), this procedure has not so far led to groups of birds being maintained in full egg production over extended periods. The most useful estimates of amino acid requirements have therefore come from feeding trials which employed semi-practical diets. The main difficulty arising in such trials is the satisfactory measurement of the levels of available amino acids being fed. In the work which is reviewed below, the availability of the limiting amino acid in a basal diet has generally been estimated by chick or microbiological assay.

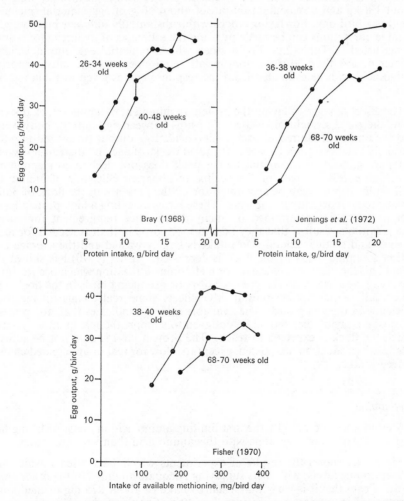

Fig. 2.3. Three examples showing the decline in utilization of protein, or of a fi.st limiting amino acid, with age.

43

Factors which affect amino acid requirements

If the requirement for an amino acid is expressed as a proportion of the diet, that requirement will be altered by all the factors which modify voluntary feed intake in the hen. Thus the concentration of protein required in the diet will increase when the energy content of the diet is increased or when the hen is kept in a warmer environment. These effects can be fully explained by the change in feed intake which occurs. There is no change in the absolute protein requirement of the bird in these situations, and the daily intakes of essential amino acids required to maximise production remain the same (Bray and Gesell, 1961; Frank and Waibel, 1960). In the sections below, amino acid requirements of laying hens are given as daily intakes and require no correction for effects of environmental temperature or of dietary energy level.

Differences between breeds and strains in amino acid requirements are closely related to differences in their body size and potential egg output (Pilbrow, 1970). The estimates given below refer to stocks with a mean body weight of about 1·8 kg and a maximum output of about 50 g of egg material (including shell) per bird day. For laying stocks with substantially different body weights, suitable corrections can be made by using the estimates of maintenance requirements listed in Table 2.9. For a stock with a potential egg output which is greater or less than 50 g the appropriate requirement for the most important amino acids can be estimated from the response curves given in Figures 2.4 to 2.7.

The effect of stage of lay on the protein requirement of a pullet flock does not show the same straightforward relationships between egg output, body weight and the amount required of each amino acid. Egg output (measured in g/day) normally reaches a peak between 30 and 40 weeks of age and thereafter declines, but the amino acid requirement of a flock does not decline correspondingly (see Figure 2.3). A part of the decline in apparent efficiency of amino acid utilisation with age can be accounted for by the presence in the flock of pullets which are not currently laying eggs. These birds are eating a high protein layers' diet in quantities determined by their maintenance requirement for energy. The inevitable result is that they take in more protein than is needed for maintenance and so their amino acid intake is largely wasted and the average utilization of amino acids by the flock is depressed. Fisher (1970) has shown that about half the decline in efficiency of methionine utilization which occurs during the laying year is due to the presence of poor producing birds in the flock. The other half of the decline presumably reflects some real change in metabolic efficiency in the aging bird. The available evidence indicates that, for practical purposes, a laying diet should be designed to support the maximum egg output which the flock is expected to reach. The protein level should not be adjusted after peak production has passed, except to allow for real or anticipated changes in feed intake.

Methionine

Methionine is commonly the first limiting amino acid in diets for laying hens and more work has been done with this amino acid than with any other.

Figure 2.4 shows the results of experiments which have used a wide range of methionine levels, with diets supplying adequate amounts of the other amino acids. From this it is clear that a daily intake of about 275 mg of methionine is sufficient to support a daily output of 40 g of egg material. However, for an output of 50 g/bird day the estimated requirement would be about 350 mg.

These figures are in reasonable agreement with the estimates of 290 mg and 340 mg, calculated from the partition equation published by Combs (1960) (assuming $W = 1\cdot8$ kg and $\Delta W = 0$):

$$M = 0\cdot05W + 6\cdot2\Delta W + 5E$$

where $M =$ methionine requirement (mg/bird day)

$W =$ average body weight (g/bird)

$\Delta W =$ rate of change of body weight (g/bird day)

and $E =$ rate of egg output (g/bird day)

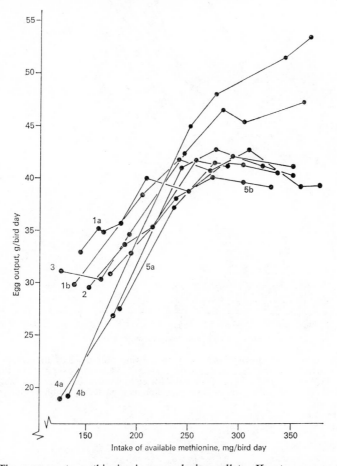

Fig. 2.4. The response to methionine in young laying pullets. **Key to sources:** 1a, b—two experiments reported by Bray (1965); 2—Combs (1962); 3—Combs (1964); 4a, b—an experiment with two strains described by Fisher (1970); 5a, b—Fisher & Morris (1970).

Lysine

Figure 2·5 shows the available evidence about responses to lysine input. Although there are many lines, it should be noted that eight of these come from a single experiment, so that the amount of independent evidence is not as great as for methionine.

45

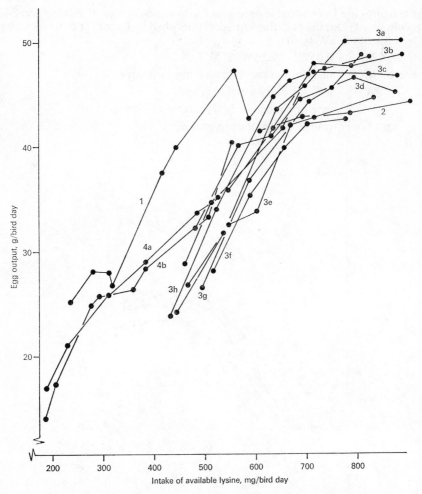

Fig. 2.5. The response to dietary lysine in young laying pullets. Key to sources: 1—Bray (1969) (data for the last two weeks of an 8-week assay kindly supplied by the author); 2—Gill *et al.* (1965); 3a . . . h—results for eight strains compared in a single experiment (Pilbrow, 1970); 4a, b—two experiments reported by Thomas (1966).

The lysine requirement for a flock with a potential output of 50 g egg material daily is seen to be about 750 mg/bird day. This is a little higher than the 710 mg which would be obtained by calculation from the equation of Thomas (1967) quoted by Combs (1968):

$$L = 0.04 + 8.6\Delta W + 12.6E$$

where   L = lysine requirement (mg/bird day)

(W, ΔW and E as given above)

46

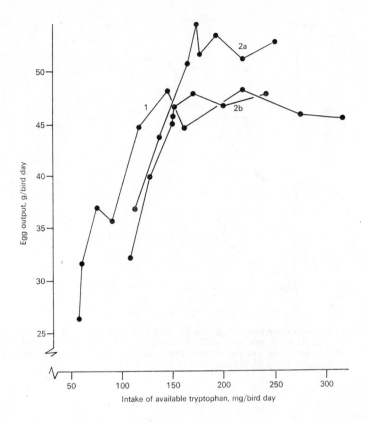

Fig. 2.6. The response to dietary tryptophan in young laying pullets. Key to sources: 1—Bray (1969); 2a, b—an experiment with two strains (University of Reading, unreported).

Tryptophan

The tryptophan requirement of the young pullet is illustrated in Figure 2.6. There are only two experiments which give satisfactory quantitative data, but these show fair agreement and indicate a requirement of about 170 mg/bird day for birds of high egg output.

Isoleucine

The single experiment by Bray (1969) is illustrated in Figure 2.7. From this it would seem that 430 mg/bird day is adequate for an egg output of 44g and that the requirement for 50 g egg output is about 550 mg/bird day.

Other amino acids

There are no satisfactory estimates of the requirement of the laying hen for the other essential amino acids. Such estimates as are available (e.g. Johnson and Fisher, 1958) often relate to birds at low levels of output and do not give enough experimental data to allow reasonable extrapolation to normal production levels. The values given in Table 2.10 are calculated from the assumed needs for maintenance and egg production purposes.

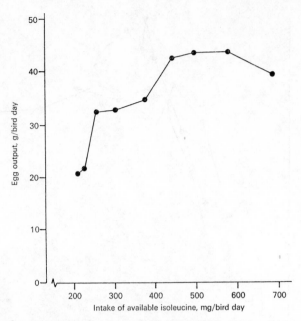

Fig. 2.7. Data from an experiment reported by Bray (1969) showing the response of young laying pullets to dietary isoleucine. The response curve refers to the last two weeks of an 8-week assay, not the average response over eight weeks, as reported in the original paper (data kindly supplied by the author).

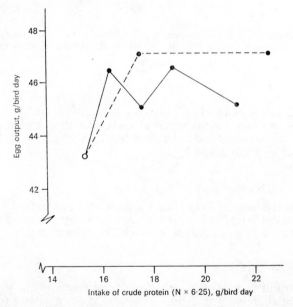

Fig. 2.8. Data from Pilbrow (1970) showing the response of young laying pullets to total nitrogen in the presence of adequate levels of essential amino acids. ○—output from an 11·5% protein basal diet containing added lysine and methionine. —●— response to additions of diammonium phosphate. – –●– – response to additions of white fish meal. All diets contained 0·8% total P and 2·9 Mcal ME/kg.

Total nitrogen

As well as supplying adequate amounts of the essential amino acids, a diet must contain enough nitrogen to supply the requirements for synthesis of the dispensable amino acids within the hen. It seems from all the available evidence that when the amino acids in laying diets are supplied entirely by intact proteins there is never an overall deficiency of nitrogen. But when low protein diets are formulated, using synthetic amino acids to make up deficiences in the natural proteins, nitrogen may become the first limiting factor.

The experiment which is illustrated in Figure 2.8 is the only one providing a satisfactory estimate of the nitrogen requirement and from this it seems that 16 g/day of crude protein are needed for an egg output of 46 g/day. The requirement for 50 g/day egg output is probably 18 g/day of crude protein.

Table 2.10

Estimates of amino acid requirements for high-producing young laying pullets. Data for methionine, lysine, tryptophan and isoleucine are taken from Figures 2.4 to 2.7; the remaining estimates are calculated from the composition of egg protein

	Maintenance requirement for 1·8 kg hen	Production requirement* for an egg output of 50 g/day	Net requirement of *available* amino acid	Concentration of *total* amino acid required in diet assuming 110 g/day feed intake and 90% availability of each amino acid
	mg/day	mg/day	mg/day	g/kg
Lysine	—	—	750	7·5
Arginine	72	441	513	5·1
Histidine	18	156	174	1·7
Tryptophan	—	—	170	1·7
Threonine	36	324	360	3·6
Phenylalanine	18	376	394	3·9
Phenylalanine + Tyrosine	54	642	696	7·0
Methionine	—	—	350	3·5
Methionine + Cystine	108	363	471	4·7
Leucine	72	609	681	6·8
Isoleucine	—	—	550	5·5
Valine	72	480	552	5·5

* Production requirement is estimated as 1·2 times the amino acid content of a 50 g egg which assumes that the net utilization of available amino acids for egg formation is 83%. The 50 g egg material includes 5 g of shell, which has been allowed for.

REFERENCES

AGRICULTURAL RESEARCH COUNCIL (1963). *The nutrient requirements of farm livestock: No. 1: Poultry.* London, HMSO
AKRABAWI, S. S. & KRATZER, F. H. (1968). *J. Nutr.* **95,** 41
ALMQUIST, H. J. & GRAU, C. R. (1944). *J. Nutr.* **28,** 325
BALDINI, J. T., MARVEL, J. P. & ROSENBERG, H. R. (1957). *Poult. Sci.* **36,** 1031
BALLOUN, S. L. (1962). *Poult. Sci.* **41,** 417
BALLOUN, S. L. & PHILLIPS, R. E. (1957). *Poult. Sci.* **36,** 884
BERG, L. R. (1959). *Poult. Sci.* **38,** 158
BHARGAVA, K. K., SHEN, T. F., BIRD, H. R. & SUNDE, M. L. (1971). *Poult. Sci.* **50,** 726
BIRD, F. H. (1950). *Poult. Sci.* **29,** 737
BLAIR, R. (1972). *Wld's Poult. Sci. J.* **28,** 189
BORNSTEIN, S. (1970). *Br. Poult. Sci.* **11,** 197
BRAY, D. J. (1965). *Poult. Sci.* **44,** 1173
BRAY, D. J. (1968). *Poult. Sci.* **47,** 1005
BRAY, D. J. (1969). *Poult. Sci.* **48,** 674
BRAY, D. J. & GESELL, J. A. (1961). *Poult. Sci.* **40,** 1328
CARPENTER, K. J., ELLINGER, G. M., MUNRO, M. I. & ROLFE, E. J. (1957). *Br. J. Nutr.* **11,** 162
COMBS, G. F. (1960). *Proc. Md Nutr. Conf. Fd Mfrs,* 28
COMBS, G. F. (1962). *Proc. Md Nutr. Conf. Fd Mfrs,* 65
COMBS, G. F. (1964). *Proc. Md Nutr. Conf. Fd Mfrs,* 45
COMBS, G. F. (1968). *Proc. Md Nutr. Conf. Fd Mfrs,* 86
DEAN, W. F. (1967a). *Proc. Cornell Nutr. Conf. Fd Mfrs,* 74
DEAN, W. F. (1967b). *Cornell University Extension Stencil* 25
DEAN, W. F. & SCOTT, H. M. (1965). *Poult. Sci.* **44,** 803
D'MELLO, J. P. F. & LEWIS, D. (1970). *Br. Poult. Sci.* **11,** 367
D'MELLO, J. P. F. & LEWIS, D. (1971). *Br. Poult. Sci.* **12,** 345
DOBSON, D. C., ANDERSON, J. O. & WARNICK, R. E. (1964). *J. Nutr.* **82,** 67
DUNKELGOD, K. E. (1968). *Diss. abstr. (B)* **29,** 822B
EDWARDS, H. M., NORRIS, L. C. & HEUSER, G. F. (1956). *Poult. Sci.* **35,** 385
FAO (1970). FAO Nutrition Study No. 24. Food and Agriculture Organisation, Rome
FISHER, C. (1970). Ph.D. thesis, Univ. Reading
FISHER, C. & MORRIS, T. R. (1970). *Br. Poult. Sci.* **11,** 67
FITZSIMMONS, R. C. & WAIBEL, P. E. (1962). *Poult. Sci.* **41,** 260.
FRANK, F. R. & WAIBEL, P. E. (1960). *Poult. Sci.* **39,** 1049.
GILL, R., PAYNE, C. G. & LEWIS, D. (1965). *Univ. Nottingham Sch. Agric. Report,* 89
GRABER, C., ALLEN, N. K. & SCOTT, H. M. (1970). *Poult. Sci.* **49,** 692
GRIMINGER, P. & SCOTT, H. M. (1959). *J. Nutr.* **68,** 429
HARPER, A. E., BENEVENGA, N. J. & WOHLHUETER, R. M. (1970). *Physiol. Rev.* **50,** 428
HARPER, A. E. & ROGERS, Q. R. (1965). *Proc. Nutr. Soc.* **24,** 173
HARVEY, D. (1970). *Tables of the amino acids in foods and feedingstuffs.* Technical Communication 19, Commonwealth Bureau of Animal Nutrition, Bucksburn, Aberdeen
HEWITT, D. (1968). Ph.D. thesis, Univ. Nottingham
HEWITT, D. & LEWIS, D. (1972a). *Br. Poult. Sci.* **13,** 449
HEWITT, D. & LEWIS, D. (1972b). *Br. Poult. Sci.* **13,** 465
JENNINGS, R. C., FISHER, C. & MORRIS, T. R. (1972). *Br. Poult. Sci.,* **13,** 279
JOHNSON, D. & FISHER, H. (1958). *Br. J. Nutr.* **12,** 276
KANDATSU, M. & ISHIBASHI, T. (1966). *Proc. 13th Wld's Poult. Cong.,* 173
KLAIN, C. J. & JOHNSON, B. C. (1962). *J. biol. Chem.* **237,** 123
KRATZER, F. H. & WILLIAMS, D. E. (1948). *J. Nutr.* **35,** 315
KRATZER, F. H., WILLIAMS, D. E. & MARSHALL, B. J. (1949). *J. Nutr.* **37,** 337
KRATZER, F. H., WILLIAMS, D. E. & MARSHALL, B. J. (1951). *J. Nutr.* **43,** 223
KRATZER, F. H., WILLIAMS, D. E. & MARSHALL, B. J. (1952). *J. Nutr.* **47,** 63
LEE, P. J. W., GULLIVER, A. J. & MORRIS, T. R. (1971a). *Br. Poult. Sci.* **12,** 413
LEE, P. J. W., GULLIVER, A. J. & MORRIS, T. R. (1971b). *Br. Poult. Sci.* **12,** 499
LEVEILLE, G. A. & FISHER, H. (1959). *J. Nutr.* **69,** 289

LEVEILLE, G. A. & FISHER, H. (1960). *J. Nutr.* **70,** 135
LEVEILLE, G. A., SHAPIRO, R. & FISHER, H. (1960). *J. Nutr.* **72,** 8
LILLIE, R. J. & DENTON, C. A. (1966). *Poult. Sci.* **45,** 810
LILLIE, R. J. & DENTON, C. A. (1967). *Poult. Sci.* **46,** 1550
MORRIS, T. R. (1972). In *Egg formation and production.* Ed. B. M. Freeman & P. E. Lake. Edinburgh, British Poultry Science
NATIONAL RESEARCH COUNCIL (1971). *Nutrient requirements of poultry*, NRC Publication 1345. Washington DC, National Academy of Sciences
PILBROW, P. J. (1970). Ph.D. thesis, Univ. Reading
ROBERTSON, R. H. & FRANCIS, D. W. (1966). *Poult. Sci.* **45,** 324
SCHWARTZ, H. G., TAYLOR, M. W. & FISHER, H. (1958). *J. Nutr.* **65, 25**
SCOTT, M. L., HILL, F. W., PARSONS, E. H., BRUCKNER, J. H. & DOUGHERTY, E. (1959). *Poult. Sci.* **38,** 497
SHERMAN, W. C., DONOVAN, G. A. & REYNOLDS, W. M. (1960). *Poult. Sci.* **39,** 1293
SNETSINGER, D. C. (1967). In *Protein utiilization by poultry.* Ed. R. A. Morton & E. C. Amoroso. Edinburgh, Oliver & Boyd
SNETSINGER, D. C., BRITZMAN, D. G., FITZSIMMONS, R. C. & WAIBEL, P. E. (1964). *Poult. Sci.* **43,** 675
SUMMERS, J. D., PEPPER, W. F., SLINGER, S. J. & MCCONACHIE, J. D. (1967). *Poult. Sci.* **46,** 1158
THOMAS, O. P. (1966). *Proc. Md Nutr. Conf. Fd Mfrs*, 80
THOMAS, O. P. (1967). *Feedstuffs*, **39,** No. 1, 19
UWAEGBUTE, H. O. & LEWIS, D. (1966). *Br. Poult. Sci.* **7,** 249
WAIBEL, P. E. (1959). *Poult. Sci.* **38,** 712
WALDROUP, P. W. & HARMS, R. H. (1962). *Bull. Fla agric. Exp. Stn*, **646**
ZIMMERMAN, R. A. & SCOTT, H. M. (1965). *J. Nutr.* **87,** 13

CHAPTER 3

REQUIREMENTS FOR MINERALS

CALCIUM AND PHOSPHORUS

Calcium and phosphorous interact with one another both before and after absorption from the digestive tract and excessive amounts of either mineral will interfere with the utilization of the other. The requirements for both calcium and phosphorus are influenced by the level of dietary vitamin D and, in general, the requirements for calcium and phosphorus increase as the level of vitamin D decreases and *vice versa*, although there are obviously levels of these minerals below which no amount of vitamin D will provide compensation.

Much of the phosphorus in cereal grains, leguminous seeds and other feeds of plant origin is present in the form of salts of phytic acid. The availability of phytate phosphorus to farm livestock has been the subject of much controversy and there is still no general agreement on the extent to which it can provide for the phosphorus requirements of poultry. Our assessment of the literature is that the availability of phosphorus combined in this form for young chicks and laying hens (but not for growing pullets) is negligible at dietary levels of calcium high enough to permit maximum bone or egg shell calcification, although it can be considerable at lower levels of calcium. We give our recommendations in terms of "non-phytate phosphorus" and suggest that phytate phosphorus is considered to be completely unavailable when practical diets are being formulated for chicks or laying hens.

The presence of phytate in poultry diets creates a further problem. Calcium phytate is very insoluble and calcium bound in this form is poorly available, so that requirements for calcium increase as the level of phytate in the diet increases.

CRITERIA FOR ASSESSING REQUIREMENTS

Growing poultry

The requirements for calcium and phosphorus for chicks, poults and older growing stock are determined by measuring either the rate of growth, the ash percentage of the bones or the composition of the bone ash. The maximum value for each of these parameters is not always given by the same dietary concentrations of minerals. It is usually found, for example, that greater amounts of dietary calcium are required for maximum bone ash percentage than for maximum growth, although the requirement for phosphorus is similar for both. Accordingly, in making recommendations, a range of values is given for these elements in most cases, which obviates the unwarranted suggestion of precision implicit in a single figure, but at the same time discourages the use of excessive amounts of minerals in the diet.

The requirement for calcium by older growing pullets (8 to 18 weeks of age) should not be judged simply in terms of the amount for normal growth, but should also be assessed in terms of the subsequent laying performance of those pullets.

In reviewing the literature concerned with the requirements of chicks and young stock for calcium and phosphorus one is struck by the wide variations between estimates made by different authors. Differences in the experimental diets, stock and environment and in the criteria used for assessing the responses all influence the results. However, the greatest single factor responsible for variations between experiments is, in general, the metabolizable energy content of the diets. By expressing the calcium and phosphorus contents of the diets in terms of ME it is possible to compare experiments more readily.

When dose-response curves relating dietary levels of calcium or phosphorus to some criterion of performance are constructed it is often found that these curves are of the "diminishing response" type, showing no genuine plateaux. This makes it difficult to decide what concentration of a mineral gives a response sufficiently near the maximum for it to be considered optimal. Here again the system of giving a range of values can be useful. Whenever the experimental data are sufficient to permit the construction of dose-response curves, these have been used for estimating requirements, rather than the original authors' selected values.

Laying hens

The main criteria used for determining the requirements of calcium and phosphorus for laying hens are egg production and shell thickness (or some indirect estimate of shell thickness).

The requirements of laying birds for most nutrients are seldom more than two or three times that of non-laying birds of the same age, but requirements for calcium are twenty or thirty times greater for layers than for non-layers. Furthermore, the daily calcium requirements for egg shell formation bear little relation to body weight. Voluntary feed intake, however, is closely related to live-weight, with the result that laying diets formulated for small birds must contain higher levels of calcium than those designed for heavy birds. It is not satisfactory, therefore, to state the requirements of laying hens for calcium in the same way as for other nutrients, that is in terms of a concentration in the diet or as a ratio to dietary energy. A more satisfactory method of stating the requirements for calcium is to specify the weight of the element required per bird per day during egg shell formation.

Ultimately, however, a requirement for calcium stated in this manner must be translated into terms of the level of calcium in the diet, and this requires a knowledge of the daily feed intake of the birds for which the diet is being formulated. Laying hens consume approximately 20% more feed on egg-forming than on non-egg-forming days (Morris and Taylor, 1967), and the calculated dietary level of calcium should take account of this.

Most of the reports in the literature concerned with the effects of dietary levels of calcium and phosphorus on egg production describe their results in terms of the percentage composition of the diets. Where data for food consumption are given we have recalculated the results to give values for daily intakes. Compared with calcium, requirements for phosphorus for egg production are relatively small, but it is nevertheless convenient to consider the two elements on the same basis.

It is only practicable to provide for the full estimated requirements of laying hens for calcium if all of it is incorporated in the diet. When lower concentrations of calcium are included in the feed and the balance is provided in the form of a calcareous grit, it is not possible to ration the birds with any degree of accuracy and a generous excess of the grit must be given.

The practice of including all the calcium in the diet is one that has become increasingly common in recent years and it may well be a system that is here to stay. It is a system that may be more easily justified on the basis of its general convenience than on nutritional grounds, and it has not yet been fully evaluated

53

in comparison with the traditional method of supplying calcium. We are not in a position to make a recommendation as to which is the better system, but if calcareous grit is to be provided at all there would not appear to be any advantage in including in the diet more calcium than is required on days when egg-formation is not taking place (perhaps 10 g Ca/kg of diet).

Since under practical conditions laying birds are fed as a flock and since in any one flock egg production in individual birds may vary from 0 to 100% it is not appropriate to vary the calcium content of the diet according to the mean level of egg production of the flock if the full requirements of the highest producers are to be provided for.

We have not attempted to calculate the calcium requirements of laying birds using average values for the percentage retention of calcium and for the amount of calcium present in the average egg shell, since both these values are highly variable. We have preferred to base our recommendations on the results of

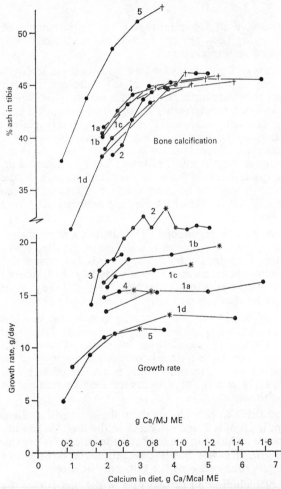

Fig. 3.1. Growth and bone calcification of chicks fed different levels of dietary calcium. Key to sources: 1a, b, c, d—four experiments reported by Edwards *et al.* (1960); 2—Edwards *et al.* (1963); 3—Twining *et al.* (1965); 4—Waldroup *et al.* (1962); 5—White-Stevens *et al.* (1960).

54

feeding experiments in which at least four different levels of calcium were included and with a minimum of fifty birds on each treatment. Somewhat less stringent criteria have been used for phosphorus.

CALCIUM AND PHOSPHORUS REQUIREMENTS OF GROWING CHICKENS

Calcium requirements up to 4 weeks of age

There are many experiments reported in the literature on the effects on growth and bone mineralisation of diets containing varying amounts of calcium. Not all of them are suitable for the present purpose however; in some the numbers of birds used on each treatment were insufficient, in others the levels of phosphorus were altered as well as the levels of calcium, while others studied too few different levels to permit the construction of adequate dose-response curves. The results of eight different experiments published since 1960 are shown in Figure 3.1, in which growth rate and percentage bone ash are related to dietary calcium level. Available phosphorus levels were considered to be adequate in all these experiments. Although most of the trials were carried out with broiler chicks, a wide range of growth rates was observed. However, since the minimal level of calcium showing maximal growth did not appear to be related to growth rate it seems reasonable to conclude that the requirements for growth are probably similar for all strains of chicken. The minimum levels of calcium showing maximum or near-maximum growth are marked in Figure 3.1 with an asterisk and those for bone-ash percentage with a dagger. The mean and median of these values for growth are 3·85 and 3·81 g/Mcal ME respectively (0·92 and 0·91 g/MJ ME) and for bone-ash 4·66 and 4·59 g/Mcal (1·11 and 1·10 g/MJ). However, the rate of increase of bone-ash percentage above 3·8 g/Mcal ME is very low and, since the calcium level of 3·85 g/Mcal ME (0·92 g/MJ) giving maximum growth rate also permits the development of well-calcified bones it does not appear necessary to exceed this level in practice in order to obtain the very marginal increase in calcification that would be expected to result from such an increase.

The experimental results used in arriving at a value for the estimated calcium requirements of chicks were obtained with diets containing amounts of vitamin D_3 not greatly in excess of requirements (400 to 600 i.u./kg). If sub-optimal levels of calcium are given, the growth rate can be maintained by increasing the amount of vitamin D_3. Thus, it has been shown by Waldroup, Stearns, Ammerman and Harms (1965) that when chicks are given a diet containing 10 g Ca/kg the requirement for vitamin D_3 for maximum growth and bone mineralisation was no more than 200 i.u./kg but that when the calcium level was reduced to 5 g/kg the vitamin D_3 requirement increased to 1600 i.u./kg (see Table 4.3). At this level of vitamin D_3 growth was as good as at the higher calcium level but bone-ash percentage was much reduced and even at a level of 16 000 i.u./kg it was still poor.

Requirements for calcium will increase as the level of phytate phosphorus in the diet increases. We suggest that, once the level of calcium appropriate to a particular dietary formulation has been calculated, this level should be increased by 1·3 g/kg for each 1 g/kg of phytate phosphorus present in the diet in excess of 2 g/kg. For example, if a diet contains 5g of phytate phosphorus per kg, the calculated calcium requirement should be increased by $(5 - 2) \times 1·3 = 3·9$ g/kg. This suggested correction is based on the assumption that each atom of phytate phosphorus chelates 1 atom of calcium (Griffith and Young, 1967).

Phosphorus requirements up to 4 weeks of age

Similar criteria were used in selecting the experimental results to be used in assessing requirements for phosphorus to those used for calcium. The data used are summarised in Figure 3.2. Again, growth rate and percentage bone-ash

55

are used for comparing the adequacy of the different diets and g non-phytate phosphorus/Mcal ME is used as a measure of dietary phosphorus levels. None of the diets was limiting in calcium. In some experiments maximum bone-ash percentage was achieved at a level of dietary phosphorus lower than that which permitted maximum growth and in other experiments the opposite was observed. It seems probable that chance played a large part in these results and that there is no real difference between the phosphorus requirements for maximum growth and for maximum calcification of the bones. For the five experiments in Figure 3.2 in which a growth plateau was reached, the average level of non-phytate phosphorus required, either for maximum growth or maximum bone-ash percentage, was 1·56 g non-phytate P/Mcal ME (0·37 g/MJ). This corresponds to 4·7 g/kg non-phytate P in a diet containing 3·0 Mcal ME/kg (12·6 MJ/kg).

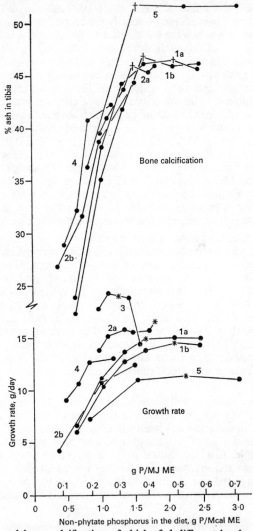

Fig. 3.2. Growth and bone calcification of chicks fed different levels of non-phytate phosphorus. Key to sources: 1a, b—two experiments reported by Gardiner (1962); 2a, b—two experiments reported by Nott (1967); 3—Twining *et al.* (1965); 4—Waldroup, Stearns, *et al.* (1965); 5—White-Stevens *et al.* (1960).

56

The phosphorus supplements used in these experiments, sodium, potassium and dicalcium phosphates, are known to be highly available to the chick, but the phosphorus in crude mineral phosphates such as raw rock phosphate and colloidal phosphate is of much lower availability than the pure orthophosphates used experimentally. The crude materials are also somewhat variable in their total content of phosphorus and these factors must be taken into account if these supplements are used. Hydrated secondary calcium phosphate, the form commonly used as a supplement in practical diets, is more highly available than the anhydrous form (Gillis, Edwards and Young, 1962).

Calcium and phosphorus requirements from 4 to 16 weeks of age

Hijikuro and Morimoto (1966) studied the calcium and phosphorus requirements of White Leghorn chicks from 4 to 8 or 4 to 10 weeks of age, using diets containing 5, 7·5, 10 and 12·5 g Ca/kg and 4·8, 6·0 and 7·2 g total phosphorus/kg in all twelve combinations. In their first trial only 12·5 g Ca/kg at the two lower levels of phosphorus gave growth and food conversion rates significantly less than for the other ten dietary combinations; differences between treatments in bone ash were small. In a second trial the only significant difference in performance with pullets was due to reduced growth on the diet containing the highest level of calcium combined with the lowest level of phosphorus. With males, however, only 7·5 g Ca/kg gave maximum performance at all levels of phosphorus, although apart from the diets containing 10 and 12·5 g Ca/kg together with 4·8 g P/kg and the one containing 5 g Ca/kg and 6 g P/kg in which growth was reduced, all the others promoted growth at rates not significantly different from one another.

O'Rourke, Phillips and Cravens (1952, 1955) have investigated the phosphorus requirements of growing pullets. Using purified diets supplying 4·07 Mcal ME/kg (17·0 MJ/kg) they established that 2·7 g/kg inorganic phosphorus was the minimum requirement during the 4 to 10 week stage. In later experiments in which practical maize-soya diets containing 10 g Ca/kg were used with oyster shell provided *ad libitum*, it was concluded that 6 g total phosphorus/kg was required for birds from 4 to 10 weeks of age, while 5 g total phosphorus/kg was required from 8 to 20 weeks to achieve normal growth. Age at first egg, percentage egg production and egg weight were the same with 4 g/kg as with 5 or 6 g total phosphorus/kg, although growth was slightly depressed at the lowest level. It should be stated, however, that all these trials were carried out on a relatively small scale, the groups were not properly replicated and the practical diets supplied excessive amounts of calcium.

Berg, Bearse and Merrill (1964), using a diet based mainly on sucrose and soya-bean meal which provided 3·21 Mcal ME/kg (13·4 MJ/kg), concluded that replacement pullets whether reared on wire or litter required no more than 4 g Ca/kg and 3 g total phosphorus/kg, all of plant origin, from 8 to 21 weeks of age. These experiments were carried out on a large scale and the criteria used were growth, bone ash and laying performance. In one experiment, 3·6 g Ca/kg and 2·8 g total phosphorus/kg gave results as good as those obtained when higher levels of these elements were given. At this low level of calcium a large proportion of the phytate phosphorus in the diet should have been available.

It is not possible to determine precise requirements from these data, but it is clear that requirements for both calcium and phosphorus are less from 4 weeks of age than during the 0 to 4 week stage.

Our preferred estimates for birds between 4 and 8 weeks of age are 7·5 g Ca/kg and 6 g total phosphorus/kg, although both these estimates may be high. For birds from 9 to 16 weeks of age we suggest 4 g Ca/kg and 3 g total phosphorus/kg.

Harmful effects of high-calcium diets for growing pullets

The rate at which pullets retain calcium from the diet increases greatly about two weeks before the first egg is laid and it is important therefore to ensure that their calcium intake at this time is sufficient to meet their increased requirements. This may be achieved either by providing calcareous grit or by changing them from a growers' to a layers' diet. This change-over is usually made at about 18 weeks of age and there is evidence that harm may result if growing pullets are given a high-calcium diet too early. Thus, Shane, Young and Krook (1968) showed that 50% of pullets reared on a diet containing 30 g Ca/kg and 4 g available phosphorus/kg from 8 weeks of age showed severe renal fibrosis and atrophy. The mortality rate attributed to renal failure and visceral gout was 10% during the latter part of the rearing period. These workers showed that the harmful effects of high-calcium diets could be prevented by increasing the available phosphorus to 12 g/kg but no intermediate levels of phosphorus were studied.

There is no experimental evidence to indicate the minimum age at which pullets can safely be given a high-calcium low-phosphorus layers diet but on purely theoretical grounds it can be stated that no possible benefit can be expected from introducing pullets to a layers diet before the onset of reproductive activity, i.e. before the ovary starts to develop and that the longer the period between the introduction of a high-calcium diet and the development of the ovary the greater will be the danger of kidney damage.

CALCIUM AND PHOSPHORUS REQUIREMENTS OF ADULT FOWLS

Calcium requirements of laying hens

The data from five experiments have been used to estimate the effect of mean daily calcium intake upon rate of egg production with the results illustrated in Figure 3.3. From this it can be seen that the requirement for calcium for maximum egg output is not more than 3·0 g/hen day. As this is somewhat lower than the requirement for maximum shell thickness, it turns out that the practical requirement for calcium is determined by the amount needed for shell formation, rather than the amount needed to ensure maximum ovulation rate or yolk size.

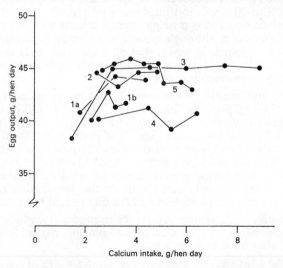

Fig. 3.3. The effect of calcium intake on egg production. Key to sources: 1a, b—two experiments reported by Davidson & Boyne (1970); 2—Helbacka (1961) and Combs (1962); 3—MacIntyre *et al.* (1963); 4—Petersen *et al.* (1960); 5—Sanford (1964).

58

For purposes of comparing different experiments which have reported the effects of dietary calcium on egg shell thickness, we have calculated weight of shell per unit of surface area (mg/cm²), assuming this to be the best common measure of shell strength that can be derived from the published data (Tyler Geake, 1961). It would have been desirable to record a standard measure of shell strength for each of these experimental treatments but no such standardisation has yet been agreed. The results for shell thickness are shown in Figure 3.4. Perhaps the most striking point to note is that in all the experiments, the thickest shells were obtained with the highest intakes of calcium. However, while the response to additional calcium was very marked with intakes of less than 3 g, the response to intakes above 3·8 g was quite marginal and above 5g negligible. There is some evidence that voluntary feed intake may be depressed when diets containing high levels of calcium are given (Sanford, 1964) and levels of intake greater than 5 g/day cannot be recommended.

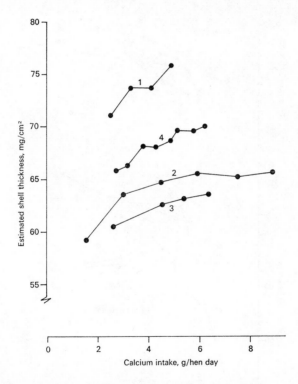

Fig. 3.4. The effect of calcium intake on estimated egg shell thickness. Key to sources: 1—Helbacka (1961) and Combs (1962); 2—MacIntyre *et al.* (1963); 3—Petersen *et al.* (1960); 4—Sanford (1964).

The experiments shown in Figure 3.4 were carried out with diets containing approximately 2 g phytate P/kg and it is to be expected that calcium requirements will increase as dietary phytate increases. Since there are no experimental data for laying birds on which to base quantitative recommendations we suggest that the same correction should be made as for young chicks; that is, 1·3 g Ca/kg should be added for each 1 g phytate P/kg in excess of a basic 2 g/kg.

59

Phosphorus requirements of laying hens

It is known that phosphorus requirements for hens kept on wire floors are greater than for birds housed on litter, presumably because the latter are able to supplement their dietary source by eating the litter. The results of experiments on the requirements for phosphorus have therefore been considered separately for the two conditions of husbandry and are summarised separately in the upper and lower parts of Figure 3.5. All these experiments were long term, many over 300 days in duration and all over 125 days. The various levels of dietary phosphorus have been calculated in terms of "non-phytate phosphorus" which is virtually the same as inorganic phosphorus. The mean value for the minimum levels of phosphate giving maximum or near-maximum egg-production for the experiments with hens maintained in cages (marked with asterisks in the Figure) is 0·39 g/hen day and the median 0·30 g. The corresponding values for hens on litter are 0·32 g and 0·29 g/hen day.

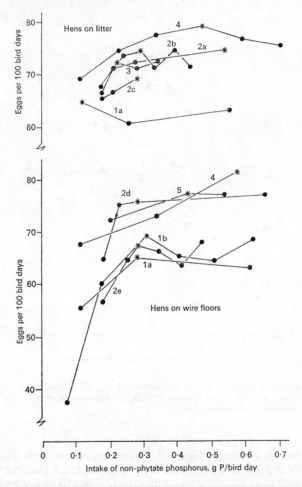

Fig. 3.5. The effect of phosphorus intake on rate of lay. Key to sources: 1a, b—two experiments reported by Crowley *et al.* (1963); 2a, b, c, d, e—five experiments reported by Harms *et al.* (1961); 3—Pepper *et al.* (1959); 4—Singsen *et al.* (1962); 5—Walter & Aitken (1962).

60

Breeding males

Concern is sometimes expressed that, when the breeding flock is given a high-calcium diet, the fertility of the males may suffer due to a reduction in the availability of trace elements, notably of zinc and manganese. What little evidence is available (Wilson, Persons, Rowland and Harms, 1969) does not suggest that this danger is serious, but it is certainly one that should be borne in mind. The easiest way of avoiding it would be to include only moderate amounts of calcium in the breeders' diets (*circa* 10 g/kg) and to provide calcareous grit *ad libitum*.

CALCIUM AND PHOSPHORUS REQUIREMENTS OF TURKEYS

Poults up to 8 weeks of age

In all the experiments relevant to an assessment of the calcium and phosphorus requirements of young turkeys, both elements were studied together, and it is appropriate therefore that the same procedure should be followed here. Turkey poults are peculiarly sensitive to a deficiency of phosphorus, and an excess of calcium can readily depress growth by inducing a phosphorus deficiency. For example Neagle, Blaylock and Gould (1968) found that the mean 4-week weight of poults given diets containing 8 g Ca/kg, 6 g P/kg and varying levels of vitamin D_3 (all considered to be adequate for normal growth) was 554g but when the calcium level was increased to 16 g/kg the mean weight was 484 g for the same level of phosphorus and the same levels of vitamin D_3. Similarly, excess phosphorus depressed growth with a diet marginally deficient in calcium (6 g/kg) unless additional vitamin D_3 was given.

A study of the phosphorus requirements of young turkeys is complicated by the finding that certain sources of supplementary phosphorus are much less available than others. Thus, for example, potassium dihydrogen orthophosphate, primary calcium orthophosphate and hydrated secondary calcium orthophosphate are highly available, while tricalcium phosphate and anhydrous secondary calcium phosphate show much lower availability (Gillis, Edwards and Young, 1962; Scott, Butters and Ranit, 1962). Steamed bone flour is presumably in the latter category of phosphorus supplements. A further complication is that turkey poults grow less well on purified diets than on diets containing a proportion of natural feed ingredients, such as soya-bean meal or soya protein, so that the former diets are not suitable for assessing requirements for phosphorus (Kratzer, Vohra, Atkinson, Davis, Marshall and Allred, 1959; Wilcox, Carlson, Kohlmeyer and Gastler, 1961). Other factors in soya-beans and in oat-hulls increase the availability of the phosphorus in anhydrous dicalcium phosphate (Griffith, Young and Scott, 1966; Griffith and Young, 1967).

Because of these difficulties, the experiments which have been considered in assessing the requirements for calcium and phosphorus are those which employed conventional diets and highly available sources of supplementary phosphate. The diets used were typical maize-soya diets and it was not considered that the extent and precision of the results justified the detailed treatment used for assessing the requirements of chicks. The experimental results used in assessing the calcium and phosphorus requirements of poults are given in Table 3.1. It would appear from these results that the requirement for calcium is between 8 and 9 g/kg and for total phosphorus between 6·5 and 7·5 g/kg for diets containing 3·2 Mcal (13·4 MJ) ME/kg. A more precise assessment does not seem justified.

61

Table 3.1
Data used in assessing the calcium and phosphorus requirements of young turkeys (0-8 weeks)

Source	Author's conclusions as to requirements		Remarks
	Ca g/kg	Total P g/kg	
Blaylock et al. (1961)	8	8	Abstract only
Formica et al. (1962)	8·1	6·5	Lowest levels giving normal growth and bone calcification
Nelson et al. (1963)	8	7	7 g Ca/kg adequate for growth and food utilization, but not for maximum bone ash
Sullivan & Kingan (1963)	10	8	Poults studied up to 6 weeks of age; 5 g "available" P adequate. Value for Ca based on Ca: P ratio of 1·25
Neagle et al. (1968)	12	8	8 g Ca and 6 g total P/kg gave growth rates not significantly poorer; poults studied up to 4 weeks of age

The latter requirement represents a level of between 4·5 and 5·5 g/kg for non-phytate phosphorus based on average values for the phytate content of maize and soya-bean meal (analytical values are not given in these papers). As for chicks, the estimated calcium requirements should be increased by 1·3 g for each 1 g phytate phosphorus present per kg of diet in addition to the "basal" amount of 2 g/kg.

As a general principle we do not consider it desirable to lay undue stress on the Ca:P ratios of diets, because it tends to distract attention from the more important question of the absolute level of these minerals; but since turkey poults appear to be particularly susceptible to growth depression by excessive amounts either of calcium or of phosphorus we recommend that if for some good reason the level of one of these elements in a formulation is in excess of the estimated requirement then the level of the other should be raised so as to maintain a Ca:total P weight ratio of approximately 1·25:1.

Table 3.2
Calcium and phosphorus requirements of growing turkeys

Source		Ca g/kg	Total P* g/kg	Age (weeks)	Remarks
Blaylock et al. (1961)		4	4	16–20	
Nelson et al. (1963)	(Exp. 1)	6	6	8–20	
	(Exp. 2)	4·9	4·9	8–20	
Day & Dilworth (1962)		6	6 (3·6)	9–16	Lowest levels studied
		6	4·5 (2·1)	17–24	Lowest levels studied

* Available P in brackets where reported

62

Turkeys over 8 weeks of age

It is not possible to arrive at any precise estimates of the calcium and total phosphorus requirements of growing turkeys from the experimental data available (summarised in Table 3.2). One can say little more than that requirements for both elements are somewhat less than for young poults and that they may be as low as 5 g/kg of each from 8 to 16 weeks and 4 g/kg of each from 16 weeks onwards.

Breeding turkeys

The calcium requirements of breeding turkeys are normally assessed in terms of egg production and hatchability. Both are depressed by low levels of calcium and some studies have shown that hatchability is depressed by high levels of calcium (30 g/kg or more) (Jensen, Saxena and McGinnis, 1963; Balloun and Miller, 1964; Arends, Miller and Balloun, 1967), although this depression is not always observed (Atkinson, Bradley, Couch and Quisenberry, 1967; Jensen, Wagstaff, McGinnis and Parks; 1964). The experimental results used in assessing requirements are shown in Table 3.3. The dietary energy levels employed and the levels of daily intakes of calcium giving the best performance showed considerable variation. The requirements in terms of the weight of calcium required per day appear to be 5 to 6 g, representing a level of 22·5 to 25·0 g/kg in diets of approximately 3 Mcal (12·6 MJ) ME/kg.

Table 3.3
Estimates of the calcium requirements of breeding turkeys

Source	Dietary levels of Ca studied, g/kg	Best performance*		Dietary energy
		g Ca/day	g Ca/kg	Mcal (MJ) ME/kg
Johnson *et al.* (1963)	9·5, 17·6, 25·8, 31·6	5·07	17·6	3·31 (13·9)
Atkinson *et al.* (1967) (birds in cages)	12·4, 19·0, 26·6, 34·3	5·82	26·6	2·78 (11·6)
(birds on floor)	16·7, 24·3, 31·9, 39·5	7·37	31·9	2·78 (11·6)
Balloun & Miller (1964)	15, 20, 25, 30	5·70	20·0	3·11 (13·0)
Potter *et al.* (1966)	9·9, 17·7, 25·5, 33·3	—	17·7	?
Arends *et al.* (1967)	15, 22·5, 30	—	22·5	3·01 (12·6)

* Egg production and hatchability

No experiments have been found which were specifically designed to determine phosphorus requirements and most studies with breeding turkeys have employed diets calculated to contain 6·0 to 8·5 g total P/kg. However, Arends *et al.* (1967) found that performance on a diet containing 22·5 g Ca/kg was almost as good with 4 g as with 8 g total P/kg. On the basis of the very meagre experimental data available, the preferred estimate of requirement is 3 g/kg for inorganic phosphorus (or 5 g/kg for total phosphorus in diets containing 2 g phytate phosphorus/kg).

CALCIUM AND PHOSPHORUS REQUIREMENTS OF DUCKS AND GEESE

Very little experimental work has been carried out on the mineral requirements of water-fowl. However, the calcium requirements of ducklings for maximum growth on maize-soya diets have been shown to be 5·6 g/kg. Bone ash percentages were almost maximal at this level of dietary calcium, although small increases occurred at higher levels (Dean, Scott, Young and Ash, 1967).

The calcium requirement of goslings during the first six weeks of life would seem to be no greater than 4 g/kg (Aitken, Lindblad and Hunsaker, 1958). Growth was normal at the lowest level of phosphorus studied in these experiments (4·6 g total P/kg, including 2·0 g inorganic P/kg), so that the true requirement may be somewhat less than this.

CALCIUM AND PHOSPHORUS REQUIREMENTS OF PHEASANTS

Scott, Holm and Reynolds (1958) found that the calcium requirement of young pheasants up to the age of five weeks was 9·3 g/kg for maximum growth but that 12 g/kg was required for maximum bone calcification. Hinkson, Gardiner, Kese, Reddy and Smith (1971) agreed that 9·0 to 9·8 g Ca/kg gave optimum body weight (at 4 or 5 weeks) but found in three different experiments that 9·0, 9·8 and 10·6 g Ca/kg also gave maximum bone ash. These differences are not great and the experimental data do not warrant separate recommendations for calcium requirements for growth and for maximum bone ash. The estimate of requirements for calcium for young pheasants up to 5 weeks of age is therefore 10 g/kg of diet.

Scott *et al.* (1958) reported that 8 g total P/kg was adequate for pheasants from 0 to 5 weeks. Hinkson *et al.* (1971) did not investigate phosphorus requirements but used diets containing 8 g total P/kg.

Scott *et al.* (1958) also studied the calcium and phosphorus requirements of pheasants from 5 to 14 weeks of age and concluded that requirements at this age were no greater than 5 g Ca/kg and 4·8 g total P/kg.

In a short abstract Gardiner, Reddy and Smith (1965) reported experiments in which laying pheasants were given diets containing 10, 25 and 40g Ca/kg. Egg production was best with 25 g/kg and was reduced at both the higher and lower levels of calcium.

CALCIUM AND PHOSPHORUS REQUIREMENTS OF JAPANESE QUAIL

Chicks

Miller (1967) reared quail chicks from day-old to 6 weeks of age on 12 diets differing only in their content of calcium and phosphorus. Calcium ranged from 4·4 to 23·0 g/kg and total phosphorus from 5·9 to 11·8 g/kg of diet. There were no significant differences between treatments in growth, efficiency of food conversion or bone ash. The basal diet contained 4·4 g Ca/kg and 5·9 g total P/kg, all of plant origin, and it is possible that requirements for these minerals (particularly for phosphorus) may be even lower than these already very low levels.

Breeding stock

Experiments reported in abstract by Nelson, Lauber and Mirosh (1964) suggest that requirements for calcium may be about 25 g/kg and for total phosphorus no more than 6 g/kg, but it is not possible to make a proper assessment of the experimental results from the information provided.

MAGNESIUM

Growing poultry

Conventional feeds contain adequate amounts of magnesium and no supplementation of normal diets is necessary or desirable. Requirements for magnesium must therefore be determined using purified diets. Table 3·4 shows the results of experiments designed to determine the magnesium requirements of young chicks for growth. A requirement level of between 0·35 and 0·40 g/kg is suggested for purified diets. Phytin increases the requirement for magnesium (McWard, 1969) by up to 5 mg/kg for each additional 1 g/kg phytate phosphorus in the diet.

Table 3.4

Estimates of the magnesium requirements of chicks

Source	Minimum level of magnesium giving growth not significantly different from maximum (mg/kg)	Remarks
Gardiner *et al.* (1960) (Expt. 1)	258	358 mg/kg gave higher weights
(Expt. 2)	252	max. wt at 302 mg/kg
McWard & Scott (1961b) (Expt. 1)	225*	max. wt at 450 mg/kg
(Expt. 2)	200*	max. wt at 375 mg/kg
(Expt. 3)	200*	max. wt at 275 mg/kg
Keene & Combs (1962) (with antibiotic)	265	
(without antibiotic)	300	
Nugara & Edwards (1963) (12 g Ca/kg, 6 g total P/kg)	295	lower requirements with 6 g Ca/kg or with 12 g Ca/kg and 3 g P/kg
(12 g Ca/kg, 9 g total P/kg)	420	

* These diets may have been slightly deficient in inorganic phosphate

Two studies concerned with the magnesium requirements of young turkeys have been published (Keene and Coombs, 1962; Sullivan, 1962). The former reported a requirement for normal growth of 0·42 g/kg and the latter 0·476 g/kg and it is suggested that the mean of these values be taken as a provisional requirement.

The magnesium requirements of older growing chickens and turkeys do not appear to have been studied.

The magnesium requirements of ducklings from 2 to 14 days have been studied by van Reen and Pearson (1953) using purified diets. From calculated dose/response regression lines they estimated the requirements to be between 0·46 and 0·50 g/kg.

Laying poultry

Hajj and Sell (1969) studied the magnesium requirements of laying hens using semi-purified diets and found that 0·155 g/kg was required to maintain production, 0·275 g/kg to maintain high productivity and hatchability and 0·375 g/kg to maintain egg size. Another estimate (McWard, 1967) was that requirements for egg production are in the range from 0·49 to 0·90 g/kg. The diets used in the latter experiment were high in phosphorus (2 g P/kg from soya protein plus 6 g/kg from the mineral supplement) and the magnesium requirements may have been raised thereby. A provisional requirement of 0·4 g/kg for laying and breeding hens is recommended.

Magnesium requirements for breeding turkeys have not been determined.

Toxic levels of magnesium

Magnesium is a particularly non-toxic element. Chicco, Ammerman, van Walleghem, Waldroup and Harms (1967) observed that additions of 2 and 4 g Mg/kg to a basal diet containing 1·1 g/kg actually increased the growth of chicks when a calcium-deficient diet (4·5 g Ca/kg) was given. With diets containing adequate amounts of calcium and phosphorus the addition of 6 g Mg/kg slightly depressed growth. Mc Ward (1967) studied the effects on growing chicks (9 to 20 weeks of age) of diets containing 3·6, 5·9, 10·6 and 18·3 g Mg/kg. The two higher levels depressed growth and reduced food utilization and bone ash (not significantly at the level of 10·6 g/kg). The same birds were studied throughout a full laying season when given diets containing 4·8, 7·0, 12·0 and 19·6 g Mg/kg. The highest level resulted in lower weight gains, egg production, egg weights and food utilization. Production was also reduced with a dietary level of 12 g Mg/kg, but not significantly so.

Increasing the level of dietary magnesium from 2 to 4 g/kg has been reported as causing a 2·3% decrease in shell thickness and breaking strength of eggs laid by pullets maintained in cages (Gerber, 1963) and there was an interaction between dietary levels of magnesium and manganese. The only circumstance in which amounts of magnesium as high as 4 g/kg are likely to occur in practical formulations is when dolomitic limestone is used as a source of calcium.

It seems that the level of dietary magnesium which is potentially harmful is so high as to be of only academic interest. The toxic level appears to be greater than 10 g/kg for hens, but may be about 6 g/kg for baby chicks.

SODIUM AND CHLORIDE

Diets based entirely on plant products are almost invariably deficient in sodium for all classes of poultry, but contain sufficient chloride. Common salt is the normal source of added sodium in a practical diet and so, if the sodium content of the diet is adequate, it will normally be found that the chloride level is adequate also.

REQUIREMENTS FOR CHLORIDE

In purified diets it sometimes happens that sodium salts other than the chloride are used, and sodium bicarbonate has been incorporated in diets for laying hens subjected to high environmental temperatures. In these special cases, some knowledge of the requirement for chloride would be helpful.

There is, however, very little experimental evidence. Burns, Cravens and Phillips (1953a) showed that the chloride requirement of chicks fed a purified diet was less than 0·6 g/kg. On the other hand, Leach and Nesheim (1963) reported that 1·4 g Cl/kg was necessary for optimum chick growth. Until further evidence is available it seems preferable to adopt the higher figure of Leach and Nesheim as an estimate of requirement.

REQUIREMENTS FOR SODIUM

Young chicks

The results of experiments which have been carried out to determine the sodium requirements of chicks are summarised in Figure 3.6. Since the ME contents of the diets used in the various experiments differed considerably the estimated requirements have in each case been recalculated in terms of g Na/ Mcal dietary ME. Even then the differences in estimated requirements between workers, and between different experiments carried out in the same laboratory, are substantial and one can only suggest that the requirements of chicks for sodium lie between 0·4 and 0·5 g/Mcal ME. This corresponds to 1·2 to 1·5 g Na/kg in a diet containing 3 Mcal (12·6 MJ) ME/kg and would be supplied by 3·0 to 3·8 g common salt per kg of diet.

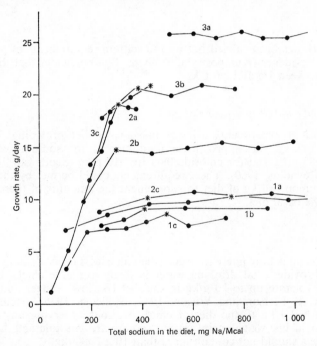

Fig. 3.6. The effect of dietary sodium on the growth of young chicks. Key to sources: 1a, b, c—three experiments reported by McDonald & Dillon (1964); 2a, b, c—three experiments reported by McWard & Scott (1961a); 3a, b, c—three experiments reported by Nott & Combs (1969).

Growing chickens

The only work that appears to have been carried out on the sodium requirements of older growing chickens is that of Anderson (1968) who found that the live-weight gain of pullets during the five-week period before the onset of lay was as great on a diet containing 0·3 g Na/kg as on diets containing 0·7 or 1·0 g/kg. There was, however, a mean delay in the onset of egg production of 2·8

67

weeks, compared with the birds given the diet containing 1 g Na/kg. These data do not allow a very precise estimate to be made of the sodium requirements of older growing birds, though they are certainly less than those of young chicks and may be as low as 0·7 g Na/kg. It is clear, too, that the requirements of females increase substantially with the onset of reproductive activity.

Laying and breeding hens

There is no reason to believe that breeding hens have a higher requirement for sodium than layers, since Burns, Cravens and Phillips (1953b) observed that a level of common salt far lower than that needed to maintain body weight and egg production did not reduce hatchability. These authors found that 1·9 g NaCl/kg (0·8 g Na/kg) was the minimum amount necessary for the maintenance of egg production and body weight using a purified diet. Kubota and Morimoto (1963) estimated the minimum requirements to be 2·5 g NaCl/kg (1 g Na/kg) and it is suggested that this level should be adopted as the estimated requirement for laying and breeding fowl.

Turkey poults

Little work has been carried out on the sodium requirements of poults, but the available evidence (Kumpost and Sullivan, 1966) indicates that the requirements are between 1·5 and 2·0 g/kg.

Pheasants and quail (0 to 4 weeks of age)

In a series of experiments using a maize-soya diet providing 2·93 Mcal (12·3 MJ) ME/kg the approximate requirements for sodium were determined as 0·85 g/kg and for chloride 0·48 to 1·10 g/kg (Scott, van Tienhoven, Holm and Reynolds, 1960). These requirements could be met by the addition of 1·5 g common salt/kg of diet to supplement the amounts of these elements present in the basal diet.

SALT TOXICITY

Salt poisoning is only likely to occur when an excess is accidentally added to the food. Provided that drinking water is freely available chicks have been observed to tolerate up to 20 g/kg in the diet (Barlow, Slinger and Zimmer, 1948; Paver, Robertson and Wilson, 1953; Sjollema, 1935). Heuser (1952) added 40 g NaCl/kg to the diet of chicks without observing any mortality or reduction in live weight gain. Turkey poults are less tolerant than chicks and their diets should not contain more than 10 g NaCl/kg.

The results of recent experiments (Dewar and Siller, 1971) have, however, raised doubts about the level of dietary sodium that should be regarded as safe for chicks and more particularly for poults. In these experiments testicular cysts were observed with diets containing amounts of sodium which had hitherto been considered safe. Birds given certain purified diets were particularly susceptible and there were differences between strains of chicken in the incidence of this condition and in the level of sodium at which a high mortality occurred. In one experiment 8 out of 12 male Broad Breasted White turkey poults fed for three weeks on a practical diet containing 4 g Na/kg showed testicular cysts on histological examination. With chicks given certain purified diets containing 5 g Na/kg, cysts developed regularly.

The physiological significance of these cysts has not yet been established and until the situation is clarified it would seem prudent not to exceed 7g Na/kg in diets for chicks and 3 g Na/kg for poults.

Adult fowl are much more resistant to salt poisoning than chicks and in one experimental situation they have been shown to withstand as much as 200 g salt/kg of diet (Blaxland, 1946).

Salt is more toxic when given in the drinking water at a specified concentration, because of the high salt intakes which result. Selye (1943) reported that a high intake of salt via the drinking water (containing about 20 g/l) caused rapid death in 2-day old chicks and that as little as 5 g/l could be harmful. This was supported by Kare and Biely (1948) who reported from an experiment with similar birds that the toxicity of sodium chloride in low concentrations in the drinking water was much the same as for an equivalent amount supplied from the mash; thus 9 g/l in the drinking water had approximately the same toxicity as 40 g/kg added to the mash.

POTASSIUM

Conventional diets are unlikely to be deficient in potassium for any class of poultry.

Chicks

The potassium requirement for chick growth was investigated by Leach, Dam, Zeigler and Norris (1959) using purified diets varying in their content of metabolizable energy. Requirements estimated by these workers for chicks from 0 to 2 and from 0 to 4 weeks of age are given in Table 3.5, and from these estimates requirements have been calculated in terms of g K/Mcal ME. These estimates are not very precise, but it is clear that requirements are greater during

Table 3.5
Estimates of the potassium requirements of chicks
(from Leach, Dam, Zeigler and Norris, 1959)

Dietary energy Mcal ME/kg (MJ ME/kg)		0 to 2 weeks of age	0 to 4 weeks of age
3·35 (14·0)	g K/kg	2·6–2·9	2·3–2·5
	g K/Mcal	0·77–0·87	0·69–0·75
	g K/MJ	0·18–0·21	0·16–0·18
3·72 (15·6)	g K/kg	3·0	2·7
	g K/Mcal	0·81	0·73
	g K/MJ	0·19	0·17
4·25 (17·8)	g K/kg	3·7	3·2
	g K/Mcal	0·87	0·75
	g K/MJ	0·21	0·18

the first two weeks after hatching than during the subsequent two weeks. It would appear from these data that requirements from 0 to 2 weeks of age are about 0·87 g K/Mcal ME (0·21 g K/MJ) and about 0·75 g K/Mcal ME (0·18 g K/MJ) from 0 to 4 weeks of age, representing 2·6 g /kg and 2·3 g/kg respectively for diets supplying 3 Mcal (12·6 MJ) ME/kg.

Poults 0 to 4 weeks of age

Sullivan (1963), using a diet of sucrose and isolated soya bean protein supplying 3·46 Mcal (14·5 MJ) ME/kg, estimated requirements for maximum growth to be between 3·2 and 3·75 g/kg. With a similar diet using glucose as the carbohydrate source, Kumpost and Sullivan (1966) estimated the minimum requirement as 3·7 g/kg.

Table 3.6

Summary of requirements for the major minerals, expressed as g/kg of diet containing 3·0 Mcal (12·6 MJ) ME/kg, unless otherwise stated. Values in italics represent preferred estimates

	Ca	non-phytate P	total P	Mg	Na	Cl	K
Fowls							
0 to 4 weeks	11·5–12·0*	4·6–4·8		0·4	1·5	1·4	2·5
4 to 8 weeks	*7·0–8·0*		*5·7–6·3*	*0·4*	*1·2*	*1·1†*	*2·5*
8 to 18 weeks	*4*		*3*	*0·4*	*0·7*	*0·6†*	*2·5*
Layers & breeders							
on wire	} *3·8–4·0‡*	{ *0·35–0·40* g/day	}	*0·4*	*1·0*	*0·9†*	*2·5*
on litter	} g/day	{ *0·30–0·35* g/day	}				
Turkeys							
0 to 8 weeks	7·5–8·5*		6–7	*0·45*	*1·5–2·0*		*4·4*
8 to 20 weeks	4·0–6·0		4–6	*0·45*	*1·5–2·0*		*4·4*
Breeders	**5·0–6·0**		5	*0·45*	*1·5–2·0*		*4·4*
	g/day						
Ducklings							
0 to 4 weeks	5·6			0·5			
Goslings							
0 to 6 weeks	4		4·6				
Pheasants							
0 to 5 weeks	10		8		0·85	1·1	
5 to 14 weeks	5		4				
Japanese quail							
0 to 6 weeks	5		4				

* Provided diet does not contain more than 2g phytate P/kg.
† Reduced from the requirement value for 0–4 week old chicks in proportion to the reduction in estimated requirements for sodium.
‡ For nearly maximum shell thickness; lower levels are sufficient for maximum rate of lay

The growth of the poults in the above experiments was poor and the mean live weights at four weeks were under 400 g. Supplee and Combs (1960) and Supplee (1965) found that requirements were somewhat higher, although the diets used were similar to those employed by Sullivan. Supplee and Combs (1960) reported that when an antibiotic was incorporated in the diet 4·5 g K/kg was required for maximum growth but 6·0 g/kg was needed when no antibiotic was given. In later experiments however (Supplee, 1965) it was found that antibiotic had no effect on the potassium requirement and that 5·1 g K/kg, the highest level given, resulted in the highest rate of growth (mean 4-week weight at this level was 561 g): it was suggested that the requirement was probably about 5·6 g/kg. The ME content of the diet used in the latter experiment was calculated as 3·83 Mcal/kg. Thus 5·6 g K/kg represents 1·46 g K/Mcal ME (0·35 g K/MJ), which corresponds to a requirement of 4·4 g/kg in a diet containing 3 Mcal (12·6 MJ) ME/kg.

The potassium requirements for other classes of stock do not appear to have been studied.

A summary of the requirements for the major mineral elements is given in Table 3.6.

TRACE ELEMENTS

The dietary requirements for trace elements cannot be stated with accuracy, since there are hardly any data for net requirement or for availability from which such values could be calculated. In this situation the results of feeding experiments must provide the estimates of requirement and although there is a fairly large number of these, the results of only two (Davis, Norris and Kratzer, 1968; Zeigler, Leach, Norris and Scott, 1961) are suitable for the calculation of requirements from a dose-response relationship. All the available data have been considered to provide the estimates of requirement given here, though in view of the nature of these data a subjective element remains in the values finally adopted.

Where possible, requirements are given for different species and ages of bird and for types of production. Other factors such as breed or strain of bird, rate of production and nature of the basal diet influence the dietary requirements of at least some trace elements and are considered, but the effects of these factors on requirements are not sufficiently well defined to permit their incorporation into tables of suggested values.

Data from which suggested requirement values have been derived are given in Tables 3.7 to 3.11. The word "sufficient" is used for values that were at least the amount required and in many cases probably exceeded the actual requirement. These were used to provide the suggested requirement values given in Table 3.12 which therefore probably err slightly above, rather than below, the true requirement. Toxic levels of some elements are given in Table 3.13.

COBALT

There are results recorded which suggest that cobalt may be required in the diet of poultry in addition to that needed as vitamin B_{12} (Turk and Kratzer, 1960), but the evidence for this is not convincing.

Cobalt is toxic at quite low concentrations in the diet. In chicks, growth is depressed by levels greater than 5 mg/kg (Turk and Kratzer, 1960).

COPPER

There are no reports of practical diets containing too little copper for poultry and the question of a requirement is only likely to arise in connection with purified diets.

The requirement for copper in both chick and layers' diets can be increased by high levels of dietary zinc. Thus Savage (1968) showed that the addition of 250 mg Zn/kg to a low-copper diet which supported only a poor rate of lay resulted in a further decrease in egg production. A similar relationship between

71

zinc and copper has been observed in chicks (Bird, O'Dell and Savage, 1963). On the other hand, the chelating agent ethylenediaminetetracetic acid (EDTA) probably increases the availability of copper. Davis, Norris and Kratzer (1962) observed a small positive growth response to EDTA, similar to that given by additional copper, when chicks were given a diet based on starch and soya bean meal.

Copper requirements can be suggested only for the chick, and there are some reservations concerning even these suggestions. Using a dried milk and sucrose diet containing 1·5 to 1·9 mg Cu/kg and additions of 1 to 7 mg/kg in different experiments, Hill and Matrone (1961) concluded from rates of growth and haemoglobin concentrations that the requirement was 4 mg Cu/kg. This value is adopted here. However, a much higher level, 14·2 mg/kg, in a starch and soya bean protein diet was reported to be slightly too low for maximum growth by Davis et al. (1962). The availability of copper of soya bean protein may be low, like that of zinc, and may be responsible for this high requirement value.

In the laying fowl, egg production and hatchability were depressed by a sucrose and separated milk diet containing 0·7 to 0·9 mg Cu/kg (Savage, 1968) but a satisfactory requirement value could not be deduced from this study since only one very high supplementary level was tested (10 mg/kg).

Turkey poults given a semi-purified diet containing 2·8 mg Cu/kg required additional copper (at least 4 mg/kg) for maximum growth in one experiment but not in another; 2·8 mg Cu/kg was sufficient for normal haemoglobin concentration and Packed Cell Volume (PCV) in both experiments (Al-Ubaidi and Sullivan, 1963).

Copper sulphate has often been added to poultry diets at levels ranging from 100 to 250 mg Cu/kg, either to protect the diet from mould growth, or with the purpose of stimulating chick or poult growth. There is little doubt that copper sulphate can stimulate chick growth in some circumstances (Smith, 1969; Jenkins, Morris and Valamotis, 1970); but in some cases there appear to be interactions between copper salts and other components of the diet which result in depressed performance (Lloyd, Jenkins, Coates, Harrison and Morris, 1971).

Concentrations of 500 mg Cu/kg and above have almost always been found to result in depression of chick growth (Mehring, Brumbaugh, Sutherland and Titus, 1960; Fisher, Wise and Filmer, 1970). Concentrations of copper below 500 mg/kg have been reported as having no adverse effects in some trials, but in other cases toxic effects have been reported with levels as low as 50 and 80 mg Cu/kg (Waibel, Snetsinger, Ball and Sauter, 1964; McGhee, Creger and Couch, 1965). The level of copper which proves toxic to chicks or poults therefore varies considerably and seems to depend on the nature of the diet in which the copper is incorporated (Supplee, 1964; Lloyd et al., 1971).

FLUORINE

There is no clear evidence that fluorine plays an essential role in the metabolism of poultry, but it is important as a toxic element.

Many studies have shown the toxic effect of fluorine (Mitchell and Edman, 1952), attention being given primarily to the fluorine in rock phosphate which is as toxic as sodium fluoride, and considerably more so than calcium fluoride (Kick, Bethke and Record, 1933; Gardiner, Parker and Carrick, 1959). Most observations have been made with chicks in which about 500 mg/kg depresses growth but 350 mg/kg has no ill-effect (Mitchell and Edman, 1952; Weber, Doberenz and Reid, 1969).

Table 3.7

Data used in assessing the copper requirements of fowls and turkeys

Source	Class of poultry and criteria of adequacy	Basal diet	Levels tested mg/kg	Conclusions	Remarks
Hill & Matrone (1961)	Chick: haemoglobin	Dried separated milk, sucrose	1·8 2·2 3·2 5·2	3·2 mg/kg sufficient	Authors concluded that requirement was about 4 mg/kg; this is the best estimate available
			1·7 2·7 4·7 8·7	4·7 mg/kg sufficient	
			1·9 2·9 4·9 8·9	8·9 mg/kg sufficient, effects of lower levels irregular	
			1·5 3·5 5·5	3·5 mg/kg sufficient	
Davis *et al.* (1962)	Chick: growth	Soya bean protein, starch	14·4 16·2 18·2	16·2 mg/kg sufficient	
Savage (1968)	Breeding fowl: egg production; hatchability	Dried separated milk, sucrose, soya bean oil	0·8 10·8	10·8 mg/kg sufficient	
Al-Ubaidi & Sullivan (1963)	Turkey poult: growth; haemoglobin; packed cell volume	Dried separated milk, casein, glucose	3·8 4·8 5·8 6·8	At least 6·8 mg/kg required for maximum growth; 2·8 sufficient for Hb and PCV	Requirement probably very similar to that of the chick
			2·8 4·8 6·8	2·8 mg/kg sufficient for growth Hb and PCV	

Egg production in adult hens was shown to be unaffected by 700 mg F/kg (Halpin and Lamb, 1932) and hatchability was unaffected by 530 mg/kg (Gerry, Carrick, Roberts and Hauge, 1949). Higher levels of fluorine were not tested in either of these studies.

Male turkey poults appear to be the class of poultry most susceptible to fluorine toxicity. Anderson, Hurst, Strong, Nielsen, Greenwood, Robinson, Shupe, Binns, Bagley and Draper (1955) reported that growth of male poults was depressed by 200 mg F/kg whilst females showed growth depression at 800 mg/kg but not at 400 mg/kg.

IODINE

No information is available on factors which may influence the availability of iodine in the digestive tract but substances (known generally as goitrogens) which influence the efficiency of iodine utilization by the thyroid gland may occur in feedstuffs. Rape seed meal contains such substances (Matsumoto, Itoh and Akiba, 1968; Clandinin, 1961) and is sometimes included in poultry diets but, although additional iodine may help, it does not completely overcome the effect of the goitrogens in rape seed.

In the absence of goitrogens, estimates of iodine requirement vary greatly with the criterion adopted for assessment of normality. In chicks, basal diets of wheat or maize with soya bean, containing 0·027 to 0·030 mg I/kg, require the addition of only about 0·050 mg/kg to give maximum live weight gain (see Table 3.7). But, to obtain thyroid glands of normal histological appearance, a total iodine content in the diet of 0·300 mg/kg is needed (Creek, Parker, Hauge, Andrews and Carrick, 1957).

Egg production is not depressed by a low-iodine diet (0·010 to 0·024 mg/kg) even when this is given throughout rearing from four weeks of age, but hatchability is low and thyroid weight of 18-day embryos large, in eggs from birds given a low-iodine diet (Rogler, Parker, Andrews and Carrick, 1961a, b). For normal thyroids of 18-day embryos it appears that 0·1 to 0·2 mg/kg is required.

Suggested requirement values for iodine are 0·4 mg/kg for the chick and 0·2 mg/kg for the breeding fowl.

Tolerance levels for iodine have been estimated as 480 mg/kg in the young chick, 180 mg/kg in older growing chickens and in laying hens, but much less in breeding hens. A level of 50 mg I/kg in the maternal diet is sufficient to impair both hatchability and the viability of newly-hatched chicks (Wilgus, Gassner, Patton and Harshfield, 1948).

IRON

The absorption of ^{59}Fe was found to be 74% in chicks given a low-iron diet containing about 10 mg/kg, but only 42% in those given a high-iron diet (Featherston, Pockat and Wallace, 1968). From two further studies still lower values were reported. Edwards and Washburn (1968) found 28% absorption with a low-iron diet and 6·3% with a high-iron diet, and Suso and Edwards (1968b; 1969) using a commercial diet recorded 7·6 to 9·8%. Two to three week old chicks were used by Featherston *et al.* and 11–12 week old birds by Edwards and Washburn (1968) and Suso and Edwards (1968b) and the difference in age

Table 3.8
Data used in assessing the iodine requirement of fowls

Source	Class of fowl and criteria of adequacy	Basal diet	Levels tested mg/kg		Conclusions	Remarks
Creek et al. (1957)	Chick: growth; thyroid histology	Wheat and soya bean meal	0·035	0·100	0·4 mg/kg sufficient for normal histology, 0·100 sufficient for growth	Large differences in requirement with criterion adopted
			0·200	0·400		
		Maize and soya bean meal	0·027	0·055	0·3 mg/kg sufficient for normal histology, 0·075 sufficient for growth	
			0·150	0·300		
Rogler et al. (1961a, b)	Breeding fowl: egg production; hatchability; thyroid weight and histology	Maize, soya bean meal	0·020	0·035	0·020 mg/kg sufficient for egg production, 0·050 for hatchability and more than 0·075 but less than 0·500 for normal histology of thyroids of embryos	Diets of some birds on low I diets changed to diets containing 0·125 or 0·250 mg/kg. These evidently gave normal thyroids of embryos
			0·050	0·075		
			0·500			

probably accounts for the difference in absorption. Thus with an adequate level of iron in the diet, absorption is in the region of 40 to 50% in very young chicks but only 5 to 10% in older birds.

Calcium as calcium carbonate and phosphate as the ammonium salt, given separately, increase the requirement for iron as judged by their effects on haemoglobin concentration (Waddel and Sell, 1964). Observations using ^{59}Fe show that these effects were caused largely by reduced availability in the digestive tract (Sell, 1965). The chelating agent EDTA tends to reduce rather than increase the availability of iron, an effect that is attributed to the very strong bonds formed between iron and EDTA (Suso and Edwards, 1968b). Davis, Norris and Kratzer (1968) found no evidence that soya bean protein reduces the availability of iron as it does with zinc.

The problem of determining a requirement increases with the number of criteria available for its assessment. Using poults given a basal diet of glucose, casein and dried separated milk containing 18mg Fe/kg, Al-Ubaidi and Sullivan (1963) found in one experiment a requirement between 38 and 48 mg/kg according to growth rate and PCV, but at least 58 mg/kg from haemoglobin concentration. In a second experiment estimates of requirement were between 38 and 58 mg/kg according to growth rate and haemoglobin but at least 78 mg/kg from PCV (see Table 3.9). For chicks, requirements recorded were 40 mg/kg by Hill and Matrone (1961), 56 mg/kg by Waddell and Sell (1964) and 75 to 80 mg/kg by Davis et al. (1968).

The requirement value for the chick suggested here is 75 mg/kg based on the data of Davis et al. (1968). The levels tested in this study were such that a dose-response relationship could be established. The requirement for the poult, from the only data available (Al-Ubaidi and Sullivan, 1963), is probably similar to that of the chick. No data are available for adult birds. There are no reports of practical diets containing too little iron.

There is no clear evidence of the toxic level of iron. McGhee, Creger and Couch (1965), using a semi-purified diet, found that as little as 100 mg Fe/kg decreased live weight slightly, but when the same diet contained 1600 mg/kg mortality was no greater than with the lowest levels tested. No data have been found on the toxicity of iron added to practical diets.

MANGANESE

Absorption and retention

The retention of manganese by chicks, as determined with radioactive isotopes, is as low as 5% or less, even when they are fed a low-manganese diet (Mohamed and Greenberg, 1943; Mathers and Hill, 1967). Similar estimates have been reported for the laying pullet (Hill, 1965). However, much higher values have been recorded using total manganese determinations in food and droppings. Woerpel and Balloun (1964) found up to 40% of dietary manganese retained in poults and Brown and McCracken (1965) reported about 32% retention in laying pullets. The latter values seem exceptionally high on considering the relation between intake and the quantity found in the egg. With a diet containing 20 mg/kg, only about 10 µg reaches the egg daily (Gallup and Norris, 1939), representing less than 0·5% of the intake. This is in keeping with the values obtained by Suso and Edwards (1968b, 1969) for the absorption of [54]Mn by chicks, which were 0·7 to 0·8% in one experiment and 2·3% in another. It is suggested that, in spite of some relatively high retention values that have been reported, the true value for poultry is less than 5%.

Table 3.9
Data used in assessing the iron requirement of fowls and turkeys

Source	Class of poultry and criteria of adequacy	Basal diet	Levels tested mg/kg	Conclusions	Remarks
Hill & Matrone (1961)	Chick: haemoglobin	Dried separated milk, sucrose	10 15 20 30 12·3 22·3 7 17 47	20 mg/kg sufficient 42·4 mg/kg sufficient, 22·3 too little 7 mg/kg sufficient	Very large variation in results among experiments. Authors suggest 40 mg/kg as best estimate of requirement
Waddell & Sell (1964)	Chick: haemoglobin	Egg white, starch	16 36 56 76 96	56 mg/kg sufficient	56 sufficient for diet containing 10 g Ca/kg and 6 g P/kg; higher levels increase requirement for Fe
Davis et al. (1968)	Chick: growth; haemoglobin; packed cell volume	Starch and soya bean protein or casein and gelatin	20 40 60 80 120 140	Requirements for growth rate, Hb and PCV were 79, 77·5 and 77 respectively. Requirement therefore given as 75 to 80 mg/kg	Data covered sufficiently wide range to permit the establishment of dose-response relationships
Al-Ubaidi & Sullivan (1963)	Turkey poult: growth; haemoglobin; packed cell volume	Dried separated milk, casein, glucose	28 38 48 58 18 38 58 78	At least 58 mg/kg required. 58 mg/kg sufficient for Hb, but at least 78 required for PCV	

When manganese as chloride, sulphate, oxide or permanganate is added to a low-maganese diet each is evidently as effective as the other in preventing manganese deficiency, suggesting that availability of manganese is similar from each source (Gallup and Norris, 1939). Some mineral oxides of manganese are poor sources of the element, compared with the sulphate (Watson, Ammerman, Miller and Harms, 1970).

Factors affecting the requirement

It has been shown that the dietary requirement for manganese is influenced by the genetic make-up of the bird. With a low-manganese diet Gallup and Norris (1939) observed an incidence of perosis of 70 to 87% in New Hampshire chicks but only 46% in White Leghorn chicks, and to achieve maximum protection against perosis the New Hampshire birds needed more manganese than the White Leghorns. A similar difference in requirement was observed for laying birds on comparing Barred Rocks with White Leghorns (Golding, Schaible and Davidson, 1940). Hatchability of eggs from White Leghorn pullets was very good with a diet containing only 9 mg Mn/kg and was not improved by the addition of manganese, whereas with the same low-manganese diet given to Barred Rock pullets hatchability was poor and was greatly improved when 50 mg/kg was added to the diet. Differences in requirement between strains of a breed have also been demonstrated (Gallup and Norris, 1939; Bolton, 1957), but no significant difference in retention of [54]Mn was found between chicks of a "light" layer hybrid and a broiler hybrid (Mathers and Hill, 1967).

There is evidence that high mineral diets reduce the availability of manganese. Wilgus, Norris and Heuser (1937a), Bandemer and Schaible (1942) and Schaible and Bandemer (1942) all showed that additions of either calcium carbonate or calcium phosphate to low (10 mg Mn/kg) or fairly low (24 mg/kg) manganese diets increased the incidence of perosis. In general, for a similar addition of calcium, calcium phosphate had a greater effect than calcium carbonate. These effects were explained as arising from absorption of manganese by undissolved or precipitated calcium phosphate or carbonate in the small intestine (Schaible and Bandemer, 1942). This proposal suggests that the reduction in availability of manganese occurs when calcium or calcium and phosphorus are present in considerable excess of requirements giving insoluble carbonate or phosphate in the digestive tract. In support of this, the replacement of part of the calcium carbonate by calcium phosphate in the diet of pullets increased the requirement for manganese at the start of lay (Longstaff and Hill, 1968) and Insko, Lyons and Martin (1938) did not observe increased perosis when bone meal or limestone was added to a diet of rather low calcium and phosphorus content.

The availability of manganese can be influenced by the nature of the protein supplement used in a semi-purified diet (Kealy and Sullivan, 1966). Poults were free of hock disorders and attained maximum weight when given 22 mg Mn/kg with dried separated milk and casein, but needed 54 mg/kg with soya bean protein. On the other hand, with a similar semi-purified diet based on soya bean protein, Watson, Ammerman, Miller and Harms (1970) reported normal bone formation and maximum growth with only 14 mg Mn/kg. Thus in semi-purified diets the protein fraction is evidently not alone in influencing manganese availability or retention.

The effect of the chelating agent EDTA has been examined but apparently it has little if any influence on the absorption of manganese (Suso and Edwards, 1968b; Vohra and Gonzales, 1969).

The availability or efficiency of retention of manganese is also influenced by the age or stage of sexual maturity of pullets. Thus birds given a low-manganese diet several weeks before point-of-lay gave poor shells but this did not occur when the same diet was given from point-of-lay (Hill and Mathers, 1968).

Requirements for manganese

In the feeding experiments referred to in Table 3.10, most basal diets contained less than 20 mg Mn/kg and in general these gave a high incidence of perosis in chicks and poults, and reduced production, hatchability or shell strength in laying birds. Some exceptional cases in which low-manganese diets had no ill-effects have been recorded (Golding, Schaible and Davidson, 1940; Chubb, 1954; Cooper, Chubb and Rowell, 1963). These exceptions are not all readily explained but it is pertinent to note that although most attention is given to recently published work, it is still necessary to rely at certain points on data obtained before consideration was given to those nutrients other than manganese which are now known to affect perosis and hatchability, and before data were routinely subjected to statistical analysis.

From a consideration of the data given in Table 3.10 manganese requirements are estimated as 50 mg/kg for chicks, poults and breeding fowls, 75 mg/kg for pheasant chicks, and 100 mg/kg for breeding turkeys. This value for breeding turkeys is very weakly founded: only one study has been reported and in this the manganese content of the basal diet was not given. For laying fowls of "light" breeds requirements are lower than those of "heavy" breeds but there is insufficient evidence to judge the size of this difference and therefore a single value, 30 mg/kg, is suggested. This is probably somewhat above the requirement for light breeds but near the correct value for heavy breeds.

Toxicity

The toxic level of manganese for poultry is not known, but it is a relatively innocuous element. 1000 mg Mn/kg caused no ill effects in chicks (Gallup and Norris, 1939) and 4000 mg/kg was fed to turkey poults without harm (Vohra and Kratzer, 1968a).

MOLYBDENUM

Although molybdenum is a constituent of the enzyme xanthine oxidase, the element is evidently required in very small amounts since it has proved difficult to demonstrate a benefit from the addition of molybdenum to most of the diets studied. Reid, Kurnick, Svacha and Couch (1965) observed a growth response in chicks and poults with only 0·0126 mg Mo/kg added to a soya bean protein chick diet containing 0·97 mg/kg or a turkey diet containing 1·58 mg/kg; but Higgins, Richert and Westerfeld (1956) used a casein diet containing only 0·02 mg Mo/kg and found no response to added molybdenum unless an antagonist was included. Somewhat similar results were obtained by Leach, Turk, Zeigler and Norris (1962). Savage (1969) found no response to added molybdenum even when using a soya bean protein diet that contained 0·7 mg/kg. The requirement for molybdenum is clearly very small—possibly less than 0·02 mg/kg.

Excess molybdenum reduces growth rate in chicks at levels of 300 to 500 mg/kg (Kratzer, 1952; Teekell and Watts, 1959; Miller and Denton, 1959) but not at 200 or 100 mg/kg (Miller and Denton, 1959; Teekell and Watts, 1959). Thus the toxic level is evidently between 200 and 300 mg/kg. Poults behave in a similar manner to chicks (Kratzer, 1952). In the adult bird 500 mg Mo/kg has only a small depressing effect on egg production but decreases embryonic survival

79

Table 3.10
Data used in assessing the manganese requirements of poultry

Source	Class of poultry and criteria of adequacy	Basal diet	Levels tested mg/kg	Conclusions	Remarks
Wilgus et al. (1937b)	Chick: growth; perosis	Maize, separated milk, fish meal	10 35 160	35 mg/kg sufficient	With NH (type G) chicks there was still 18% perosis with 50 mg/kg; no higher levels were tested with these birds
Gallup & Norris (1939)	Chick: growth; perosis	Maize, separated milk, fish meal	10 20 30 40 50 100 1000	WL 30 mg/kg sufficient; NH (type B) 50 mg/kg sufficient; NH (type G) more than 50 mg/kg required	
Pepper et al. (1953)	Chick: growth; perosis	Practical type	10 30 50	50 mg/kg evidently sufficient	
Chubb (1954)	Chick: perosis	Practical type	10 50 60	At least 60 mg/kg required in one experiment; 10 mg/kg sufficient in another	Same ingredients in basal diet of both experiments. No explanation of difference in result
Cox & Balloun (1969)	Laying fowl: egg production; shell strength and thickness	Practical type	20 53 86	20 mg/kg sufficient	
Gallup & Norris (1939)	Breeding fowl: egg production; hatchability	Maize, separated milk, fish meal	13 53 203	53 mg/kg sufficient	
Gutowska & Parkhurst (1942)	Breeding fowl: egg production; hatchability; shell strength	Practical type	17 24 61 76	17–24 mg/kg sufficient for egg production and hatchability; 61–76 mg/kg for maximum shell strength	

(continued on next page)

Table 3.10 (continued)

Source	Class of poultry and criteria of adequacy	Basal diet	Levels tested mg/kg	Conclusions	Remarks
Caskey et al. (1944)	Breeding fowl: hatachability; ataxia in chicks	Maize, separated milk, meat meal	6 36 51	50 mg/kg evidently sufficient	
Chubb (1954)	Breeding fowl: hatchability	Practical type	10 50	50 mg/kg evidently sufficient	
Cooper et al.	Breeding fowl: egg production; hatchability	Practical type	10 50	10 mg/kg sufficient	
Woerpel & Balloun	Turkey poult: growth	Maize, soya bean meal	20 64	20 mg/kg sufficient in one experiment, but more required in a second	
Kealy & Sullivan (1966)	Turkey poult: growth; leg weakness	Maize, soya bean meal	32 42 52 / 62 72 82	32 mg/kg sufficient in main experiment, slight improvement up to 72 mg/kg in a second smaller experiment	Requirement using soya bean protein was considerably greater than that using casein as the protein source
		Casein, separated glucose	2 12 22 / 32 42 52	22 mg/kg sufficient	
		Soya bean protein, glucose	9 24 39 / 54 69 84	54 mg/kg sufficient	
Atkinson et al. (1967)	Breeding turkey: egg production; hatchability; shell strength	Maize, sorghum, soya bean meal	25 52 79 / 133 187	At least 79 mg/kg required, 133 mg/kg gave slightly better hatchability	Egg production and shell strength unaffected by Mn level
Scott et al. (1959)	Pheasant chick: growth; perosis	Maize, soya bean	20 45 95 / 70	At least 70 mg/kg required, 95 mg/kg gave slightly better results	

to zero in ten days (Lepore and Miller, 1965). Thus for breeding birds the toxic level is probably considerably less than 500 mg/kg. The toxic effect of molybdenum is ameliorated by a high deitary copper level. Kratzer (1952) and Arthur, Motzok and Branion (1958) showed that the addition of 100 to 300 mg Cu/kg reduced, but did not prevent, the growth depression caused by feeding excess molybdenum.

SELENIUM

Selenium is readily absorbed by the chick (Edwards, 1969) and can markedly influence the metabolism of poultry. It can prevent exudative diathesis in the chick (Sharman, 1960), muscular dystrophy in poults and chicks (Walter and Jensen, 1963, 1964; Hutcheson, Hill and Jenkins, 1963), and a feather abnormality in poults (Supplee, 1966). It may also reduce the amount of vitamin E necessary to prevent encephalomalacia in the chick (Jenkins, Ewan and McConachie, 1965). Since all these conditions are also prevented by vitamin E (see pp 184–188) it was at one time thought that, although selenium reduced the requirement for vitamin E, no situation occurred in which selenium was essential. However, Thompson and Scott (1969, 1970), using a diet containing less than 0·02 mg Se/kg, have recently shown that atrophy of the pancreas in chicks can be prevented by administering selenium but not vitamin E. Thus selenium is now established as an essential element for the chick, though no requirement value can be given from the data available.

Selenium is a highly toxic element. In chicks, 8 mg/kg causes a small but significant decrease in growth rate (Poley, Wilson, Moxon and Taylor, 1941; Wright and Mraz, 1964). In breeding stock 2·5 mg/kg has no effect but 6 mg/kg reduces hatchability slightly and 10 mg/kg kills all embryos (Poley and Moxon, 1938). Turkeys are slightly more resistant, hatchability being unaffected by 5 mg/kg and reduced slightly by 9 mg/kg (Kohlmeyer and Moxon, 1948).

VANADIUM

The toxicity of vanadium has been investigated because of problems which may arise in poultry diets from the use of certain phosphate supplements. In a study by Berg (1963) the addition of 4 mg V/kg to a basal diet containing 6 mg/kg had no ill-effect on chicks but the addition of 8 mg/kg depressed growth. In other experiments, growth depression occurred at levels of 20 to 30 mg/kg (Romoser, Dudley, Machlin and Loveless, 1961; Nelson, Gillis and Peeler, 1962). In adult birds 15 to 20 mg/kg reduces the albumen quality of eggs, about 30 mg/kg decreases egg production, and about 50 mg/kg depresses hatchability (Berg, Bearse and Merrill, 1963b).

ZINC

Absorption and retention

Suso and Edwards (1968a) reported that chicks retained almost 20% of an oral dose of ^{65}Zn ten days after dosing and, in further experiments, absorption was found to range from 12 to 20% (Suso and Edwards, 1968b). These values are somewhat higher than those calculated for the laying bird from the percentage of dietary zinc found in the egg. Using a diet containing 32 mg/kg, Tupper, Watts and Wormall (1954) found that eggs contained 0·3 to 0·5 mg Zn, or approximately 6 to 10% of the amount ingested.

Factors affecting the requirement

The experiment of O'Dell and Savage (1957) which provided the first description of zinc deficiency in chicks, also showed that the availability of zinc in a diet containing soya bean protein was lower than that of a diet containing casein and gelatin. Further evidence of this difference in availability has been provided by a number of workers (Moeller and Scott, 1958; Morrison and Sarett, 1958; Zeigler, Leach, Norris and Scott, 1961). Also, Edwards (1966) and Miller and Jensen (1966) found greater absorption of [65]Zn from a casein or casein-gelatin diet than from a soya bean protein diet. Chicks given a soya bean protein diet also needed more zinc than those given an egg-white protein diet (Moeller and Scott, 1958). It was suggested that phytate in soya bean meal reduced the availability of zinc (O'Dell and Savage, 1960) and phytate was shown to have this effect in both chicks and laying birds (O'Dell, Yoke and Savage, 1964; Savage, 1968); but whether the lower availability of zinc in soya bean protein diets is attributable entirely to phytate is uncertain. Similar studies using sesame meal appear to discount phytate as an explanation of the very wide range of zinc availability found in different batches of this product (Turk and Lease, 1962). Heat treatment improves availability but has little effect on the phytate content (Lease, 1966) and the variation in zinc availability among samples of sesame meal is unrelated to phytate content (Lease and Williams, 1967). With cottonseed meal, however, treatment with phytase does increase the availability of zinc (Rojas and Scott, 1969), presumably by the hydrolysis of phytate to inositol and phosphate.

The use of high levels of dietary calcium carbonate has often, but not always, depressed zinc availability. These differences in results among studies probably arise from the quantities of calcium added by different workers, and also from the nature of the basal diet. In chick experiments, zinc availability was reduced when 10 g Ca/kg was added to a soya bean protein diet, but not when 5 g Ca/kg was added to a similar diet (Young, Edwards and Gillis, 1958; Roberson and Schaible, 1960a), nor when 10 g Ca/kg was added to a casein-gelatin diet (Pensack, Henson and Bogdonoff, 1958). The absence of an effect of added calcium with a casein-gelatin diet was consonant with the observation that phytate influenced the effect of calcium on availability (O'Dell et al., 1964). A high level of calcium (40 g/kg compared with 22 g/kg) in a low-zinc diet for laying hens decreased hatchability and gave weak chicks: these effects were corrected by adding zinc (Turk, Sunde and Hoekstra, 1959). The influence of calcium on zinc availability appears to be related to stage of egg production. In an experiment reported by Berg, Bearse and Merrill (1963a) a high level of calcium given from just before the start of egg production resulted in poorly feathered chicks at the start of lay and this was corrected by adding zinc to the maternal diet: but after 6 weeks of egg production the same high-calcium diet without added zinc gave almost normal chicks. The efficiency of zinc absorption or retention in birds given a high-calcium diet evidently increases as egg laying progresses. Kienholz, Sunde and Hoekstra (1964) found no decrease in the zinc content of eggs from birds given a high-calcium diet but this inconsistency with the results of Berg et al. (1963a) may have arisen from differences in details of the two experiments, in particular the time after the start of lay that eggs were collected for analysis.

The addition of the chelating agent EDTA to a low-zinc diet containing either soya bean protein (Davis, Norris and Kratzer, 1962; Vohra and Kratzer, 1968a) or phytate (O'Dell et al., 1964) increases the availability of zinc. EDTA also increases the absorption of zinc from isolated intestinal loops (Vohra and Gonzales, 1969). The toxic effect of a large concentration (2258 mg/kg) of dietary

Table 3.11
Data used in assessing the zinc requirements of poultry

Source	Class of poultry and criteria of adequacy	Basal diet	Levels tested mg/kg			Conclusions	Remarks
Morrison & Sarrett (1958)	Chick: growth	Soya bean protein, sucrose	30	35	55	35 mg/kg sufficient	Housed in galvanised brooder, water in galvanised or glass vessels made little difference
O'Dell et al. (1958)	Chick: growth; deficiency symptoms	Soya bean protein, glucose	15 28	22 38	25 78	38 mg/kg sufficient	Housed in resin coated brooder
Roberson & Schaible (1958)	Chick: growth; leg and feather development	Soya bean protein, glucose	10 50	20 90	20	30 mg/kg sufficient	Resin coated brooder
Young et al. (1958)	Chick: growth; leg and feather development	Soya bean protein, glucose	15 55	25 75	35 95	55 mg/kg sufficient	Zn-free environment
Zeigler et al. (1961)	Chick: growth; bone development	Soya bean protein, glucose	8 23	13 28 38	18 33	28 mg/kg sufficient	Zn-free environment. Dose-response relationships established for soya bean protein and casein experiments
		Casein-gelatin, glucose	5 20	10 25	15 30	15 mg/kg sufficient	
		Maize, soya bean meal	40	140		More than 40 mg/kg required	Values for basal diet calculated from authors' values for individual feedstuffs

(continued on next page)

84

Table 3.11 (continued)

Source	Class of poultry and criteria of adequacy	Basal diet	Levels tested mg/kg	Conclusions	Remarks
Turk et al. (1959)	Breeding fowl: hatchability; viability of chicks; feather development	Soya bean protein	8 58	58 mg/kg sufficient	
	Breeding fowl: hatchability; feather development of chicks	Casein	15	15 mg/kg sufficient	Birds housed in deep-litter pens
Berg et al. (1963a)		Maize, milo, barley, soya bean meal, fish meal	30 80	80 mg/kg sufficient. Requirement fell as egg laying advanced. Requirement increased by high level of Ca	
Kratzer et al. (1958)	Turkey poult: growth; perosis	Soya bean protein, starch	26 31 36 45 64 103	64 mg/kg probably sufficient, but perosis slightly less with 103 mg/kg	Galvanised feed and water troughs. No account taken of Zn from this source
Kratzer, Allred et al. (1959)	Turkey: growth; perosis	Soya bean protein, starch	25 45 65 175	65 mg/kg almost sufficient, growth slightly greater and perosis slightly less with 175 mg/kg	Galvanised feed and water troughs. No account taken of Zn from this source
Sullivan (1961)	Turkey poult: growth; bone and feather development	Soya bean protein, glucose	14 24 34 44 54 64 74	44 mg/kg sufficient for growth, 64 mg/kg for bone and feather development	Zn-free environment
Supplee et al. (1961)	Turkey poult: growth; bone and feather development	Maize, soya bean meal	33 39 45 51 57 63	51 mg/kg sufficient for growth, but more than 63 mg/kg required for normal bone and feather development	Zn-free environment
			42 92	92 mg/kg sufficient	
Scott et al. (1959)	Pheasant chick: growth; leg development	Maize, soya bean meal	42 47 52 62	62 mg/kg sufficient	

zinc is reduced by EDTA (Vohra and Kratzer, 1968b), presumably because it prevents the accumulation of large concentrations of zinc ions in the tissues.

The retention of or requirement for zinc varies with the genetic make-up of the birds. For example, the retention of ^{65}Zn was greater in New Hampshire than in White Leghorn chicks, although no marked difference in dietary requirement was observed by Martin and Patrick (1961). Abnormal feather development, which occurred in an inbred line of Ancona chicks but not in a similarly inbred line of White Leghorn chicks, was reduced to almost nil by a supplement of zinc (Englert, Jeffers, Sunde and McGibbon, 1966).

Requirements for zinc

Determinations of dietary zinc requirement are complicated by the factors discussed above, but also by the variable amount of zinc ingested from the environment other than the diet. When galvanised brooders and fittings were used in rearing chicks, Mehring, Brumbaugh and Titus (1956) estimated that zinc derived from galvanised surfaces was equivalent to 6 to 9 mg Zn/kg diet.

Table 3.12
Amounts of trace elements recorded as sufficient in Tables 3.7 to 3.11 with preferred estimates of requirement

Element	Class of poultry	Values from Tables 3.7–3.11 mg/kg diet	Preferred estimate of requirement mg/kg
Copper	Fowl, chick	3·2, 4·7, 8·9, 3·5	4
Iodine	Fowl, chick	0·4, 0·3	0·4
	breeder	0·500, 0·125	0·2
Iron	Fowl, chick	20, 47, 7, 56 75–80*	75
	Turkey, poult	58, 78	75
Manganese	Fowl, chick	35, 30, 50, 50+ 50, 60, 10	50
	layer	17–24, 50	30
	breeder	53, 17–24, 50	50
	Turkey, poult	20, 32, 72 24, 54	50
	breeder	79–133	100
	Pheasant, chick	70–95	75
Zinc	Fowl, chick	35, 38, 30, 55 27·5*, 29·2*, 12·7* 14·2*, 40+	40
	breeder	58, 15, 80	60
	Turkey, poult	64+, 65+, 64 63+, 92−	70
	Pheasant, chick	62	60

* Values derived from calculated dose-response relationships.

86

Table 3.13
Toxic levels of some trace elements

Element	Class of bird	Values reported in text mg/kg	Suggested toxic level mg/kg
Copper	Fowl, chick	>500, >500, 300	500 (see page 72)
	Turkey, poult	>910	1000
Fluorine	Fowl, chick	700, >350	400
	layer	>700	750
	breeder	>530	600
	Turkey, poult, males	200	200
	females	800, >400	500
Iodine	Fowl, chick	>480	500
	layer	>180	200
	breeder	50	50
Manganese	Fowl, chick	>1000	>1000
	Turkey, poult	>4000	>4000
Molybdenum	Fowl, chick	500, >100, 300 500, >200	} 250
	layer	<500	500
	breeder	<500	100?
Selenium	Fowl, chick	8	5
	breeder	6, >2·5	4
	Turkey, breeder	9, >5	7
Vanadium	Fowl, chick	14, >10, 20–30	12
	layer	15–20	15
	breeder	30, 80	30
Zinc	Fowl, chick	>1000, >1000	>1000
	Turkey, poult	>2000	>2000

Morrison and Sarett (1958) using a soya bean protein diet obtained zinc-deficient chicks in a galvanised brooder with water provided in galvanised or glass vessels but Edwards, Young and Gillis (1958), using a similar diet produced zinc-deficient chicks only when galvanised surfaces were resin-coated and stainless steel feed and water vessels used. Most studies of zinc conducted since the experiments of Edwards et al. (1958) have been made using equipment with zinc-free surfaces. Also in a large proportion of the studies from which requirement data are available (see Table 3.11) semi-purified glucose-soya bean protein diets were used.

The zinc content of basal diets used in zinc studies has varied widely from 5 to about 40 mg/kg and in all except two trials, in which the value was close to 40 mg/kg, improvements occurred with added zinc. Thus for the type of birds used in these trials the zinc requirement was either close to 40 mg/kg or above this.

Most observations were made using growing chicks. For other birds, only tentative requirement values can be given. The values suggested are 40 mg/kg for chicks, 60 mg/kg for breeding fowls and young pheasants, and 70 mg/kg for poults.

Toxicity

Zinc at 1000 mg/kg caused no ill-effects in chicks (Roberson and Schaible, 1960b; Johnson, Mehring, Savino and Titus, 1962) and poults have been shown to tolerate as much as 2000 mg/kg (Vohra and Kratzer, 1968b).

REFERENCES

AITKEN, J. R., LINDBLAD, G. S. & HUNSAKER, W. G. (1958). *Poult. Sci.* **37**, 1180
AL-UBAIDI, Y. Y. & SULLIVAN, T. W. (1963). *Poult. Sci.* **42**, 718
ANDERSON, J. O., HURST, J. S., STRONG, D. C., NIELSEN, H., GREENWOOD, D. A., ROBINSON, W., SHUPE, J. L., BINNS, W., BAGLEY, R. A. & DRAPER, C. I. (1955). *Poult. Sci.* **34**, 1147
ANDERSON, R. S. (1968). *Proc. Nutr. Soc.* **27**, 34A
ARENDS, L. G., MILLER, D. L. & BALLOUN, S. L. (1967). *Poult. Sci.* **46**, 727
ARTHUR, D., MOTZOK, I. & BRANION, H. D. (1958). *Poult. Sci.* **37**, 1181
ATKINSON, R. L., BRADLEY, J. W., COUCH, J. R. & QUISENBERRY, J. H. (1967). *Poult. Sci.* **46**, 472
BALLOUN, S. L. & MILLER, D. L. (1964). *Poult. Sci.* **43**, 378
BANDEMER, S. L. & SCHAIBLE, P. J. (1942). *Poult. Sci.* **21**, 3
BARLOW, J. S., SLINGER, S. J. & ZIMMER, R. P. (1948). *Poult. Sci.* **27**, 542
BERG, L. R. (1963). *Poult. Sci.* **42**, 766
BERG, L. R., BEARSE, G. E. & MERRILL, L. H. (1963a). *Poult. Sci.* **42**, 703
BERG, L. R., BEARSE, G. E. & MERRILL, L. H. (1963b). *Poult. Sci.* **42**, 1407
BERG, L. R., BEARSE, G. E. & MERRILL, L. H. (1964). *Poult. Sci.* **43**, 885
BIRD, D. W., O'DELL, B. L. & SAVAGE, J. E. (1963). *Poult. Sci.* **42**, 1256
BLAXLAND, J. D. (1946). *Vet. J.* **102**, 157
BLAYLOCK, L. G., NEAGLE, L. H. & LeFEVRE, C. F. (1961). *Poult. Sci.* **40**, 1381
BOLTON, W. (1957). *Poult. Sci.* **36**, 732
BROWN, W. O. & McCRACKEN, K. J. (1965). *J. agric. Sci., Camb.* **64**, 305
BURNS, C. H., CRAVENS, W. W. & PHILLIPS, P. H. (1953a). *J. Nutr.* **50**, 317
BURNS, C. H., CRAVENS, W. W. & PHILLIPS, P. H. (1953b). *Poult. Sci.* **31**, 302
CASKEY, C. D., NORRIS, L. C. & HEUSER, G. F. (1944). *Poult. Sci.* **23**, 576
CHICCO, C. F., AMMERMAN, C. B., van WALLEGHEM, P. A., WALDROUP, P. W. & HARMS, R. H. (1967). *Poult. Sci.* **46**, 368
CHUBB, L. G. (1954). *10th Wld's Poult. Congr. Section Papers*, 164
CLANDININ, D. R. (1961). *Poult. Sci.* **40**, 484
COMBS, G. F. (1962). *Proc. Md Nutr. Conf. Fd Mfrs*, 65
COOPER, D. M., CHUBB, L. G. & ROWELL, J. G. (1963). *Br. Poult. Sci.* **4**, 83
COX, A. C. & BALLOUN, S. L. (1969). *Poult. Sci.* **48**, 745

CREEK, R. D., PARKER, H. E., HAUGE, S. M., ANDREWS, F. N. & CARRICK, C. W. (1957). *Poult. Sci.* **36**, 1360
CROWLEY, T. A., KURNICK, A. A. & REID, B. L. (1963). *Poult. Sci.* **42**, 758
DAVIDSON, J. & BOYNE, A. W. (1970). *Br. Poult. Sci.* **11**, 231
DAVIS, P. N., NORRIS, L. C. & KRATZER, F. H. (1962). *J. Nutr.* **77**, 217
DAVIS, P. N., NORRIS, L. C. & KRATZER, F. H. (1968). *J. Nutr.* **94**, 407
DAY, E. J. & DILWORTH, B. C. (1962). *Poult. Sci.* **41**, 1324
DEAN, W. F., SCOTT, M. L., YOUNG, R. J. & ASH, W. J. (1967). *Poult. Sci.* **46**, 1496
DEWAR, W. A. & SILLER, W. G. (1971). *Br. Poult. Sci.* **12**, 535
EDWARDS, H. M. (1966). *Poult. Sci.* **45**, 421
EDWARDS, H. M. (1969). *Poult. Sci.* **48**, 1804
EDWARDS, H. M., DUNAHOO, W. S., CARMON, J. L. & FULLER, H. L. (1960). *Poult. Sci.* **39**, 1389
EDWARDS, H. M., MARION, J. E., FULLER, H. L. & DRIGGERS, J. C. (1963). *Poult. Sci.* **42**, 699
EDWARDS, H. M. & WASHBURN, K. W. (1968). *Poult. Sci.* **47**, 337
EDWARDS, H. M., YOUNG, R. J. & GILLIS, M. B. (1958). *Poult. Sci.* **37**, 1094
ENGLERT, S. I., JEFFERS, T. K., SUNDE, M. L. & McGIBBON, W. H. (1966). *Poult. Sci.* **45**, 1082
FEATHERSTON, W. R., POCKAT, T. J. & WALLACE, J. (1968). *Poult. Sci.* **47**, 946
FISHER, C., WISE, D. & FILMER, D. G. (1970). *Proc. 14th Wld's Poult. Congr.* **2**, 759
FORMICA, S. D., SMIDT, M. J., BACHARACH, M. M., DAVIN, W. F. & FRITZ, J. C. (1962). *Poult. Sci.* **41**, 771
GALLUP, W. D. & Norris, L. C. (1939). *Poult. Sci.* **18**, 76
GARDINER, E. E. (1962). *Poult. Sci.* **41**, 1156
GARDINER, E. E., PARKER, H. E. & CARRICK, C. W. (1959). *Poult. Sci.* **38**, 721
GARDINER, E. E., REDDY, D. N. & SMITH, L. T. (1965). *Poult. Sci.* **44**, 1372
GARDINER, E. D., ROGLER, J. C. & PARKER, H. E. (1960). *Poult. Sci.* **39**, 1111
GERBER, J. N. (1963). *S. African J. agric. Sci.* **6**, 381
GERRY, R. W., CARRICK, C. W., ROBERTS, R. E. & HAUGE, S. M. (1949). *Poult. Sci.* **28**, 10
GILLIS, M. B., EDWARDS, H. M. & YOUNG, R. J. (1962). *J. Nutr.* **78**, 155
GOLDING, W. V., SCHAIBLE, P. J. & DAVIDSON, J. A. (1940). *Poult. Sci.* **19**, 263
GRIFFITH, M. & YOUNG, R. J. (1967). *Poult. Sci.* **46**, 553
GRIFFITH, M., YOUNG, R. J. & SCOTT, M. L. (1966). *Poult. Sci.* **45**, 189
GUTOWSKA, M. S. & PARKHURST, R. T. (1942). *Poult. Sci.* **21**, 277
HAJJ, R. N. & SELL, J. L. (1969). *J. Nutr.* **97**, 441
HALPIN, J. G. & LAMB, A. R. (1932). *Poult. Sci.* **11**, 5
HARMS, R. H., DOUGLAS, C. R. & WALDROUP, P. W. (1961). *Univ. Fla exp. Stn Bull.* **644**
HELBACKA, N. V. (1961). *Proc. Md Nutr. Conf. Fd Mfrs*, 46
HEUSER, G. F. (1952). *Poult. Sci.* **31**, 85
HIGGINS, E. S., RICHERT, D. A. & WESTERFELD, W. W. (1956). *J. Nutr.* **59**, 539
HIJIKURO, S. & MORIMOTO, H. (1966). *Jap. Poult. Sci.* **3**, 69. Abstracted in *Nutr. Abstr. Rev.* **37** (1967) Abstr. 1834
HILL, C. H. & MATRONE, G. (1961). *J. Nutr.* **73**, 425
HILL, R. (1965). *Br. J. Nutr.* **19**, 171
HILL, R. & MATHERS, J. W. (1968). *Br. J. Nutr.* **22**, 625
HINKSON, R. S., GARDINER, E. E., KESE, A. G., REDDY, D. N. & SMITH, L. T. (1971). *Poult. Sci.* **50**, 35
HUTCHESON, L. M., HILL, D. C. & JENKINS, K. J. (1963). *Poult. Sci.* **42**, 846
INSKO, W. M., LYONS, M. & MARTIN, J. H. (1938). *Poult. Sci.* **17**, 264
JENKINS, K. J., EWAN, L. M. & McCONACHIE, J. D. (1965). *Poult. Sci.* **44**, 615
JENKINS, N. K., MORRIS, T. R. & VALAMOTIS, D. (1970). *Br. Poult. Sci.* **11**, 241
JENSEN, L. S., SAXENA, H. C. & McGINNIS, J. (1963). *Poult. Sci.* **42**, 604
JENSEN, L. S., WAGSTAFF, R. K., McGINNIS, J. & PARKS, F. (1964). *Poult. Sci.*, **43**, 1577
JOHNSON, D., MEHRING, A. L., SAVINO, F. X. & TITUS, H. W. (1962). *Poult. Sci.* **41**, 311
KARE, M. R. & BIELY, J. (1948). *Poult. Sci.* **27**, 751
KEALY, R. D. & SULLIVAN, T. W. (1966). *Poult. Sci.* **45**, 1352
KEENE, O. D. & COMBS, G. F. (1962). *Poult. Sci.* **41**, 1654

KICK, C. H., BETHKE, R. M. & RECORD, P. R. (1933). *Poult. Sci.* **12,** 382
KIENHOLZ, E. W., SUNDE, M. L. & HOEKSTRA, W. G. (1964). *Poult. Sci.* **43,** 667
KOHLMEYER, W. & MOXON, A. L. (1948). *Poult. Sci.* **27,** 670
KRATZER, F. H. (1952). *Proc. Soc. exp. Biol. Med.* **80,** 483
KRATZER, F. H., ALLRED, J. B., DAVIS, P. N., MARSHALL, B. J. & VOHRA, P. (1959). *J. Nutr.* **68,** 313
KRATZER, F. H., VOHRA, P., ALLRED, J. B. & DAVIS, P. N. (1958). *Proc. Soc. exp. Biol. Med.* **98,** 205
KRATZER, F. H., VOHRA, P., ATKINSON, R. L., DAVIS, P. N., MARSHALL, B. J. & ALLRED, J. B. (1959). *Poult. Sci.* **38,** 1049
KUBOTA, D. & MORIMOTO, H. (1963). *Bull. Nat. Inst. Animal Indust. Japan. Summaries of Reports No. 1,* 21. Abstracted in *Nutr. Abstr. Rev.* (1964) Abstr. 1650
KUMPOST, H. E. & SULLIVAN, T. W. (1966). *Poult. Sci.* **45,** 1334

LEACH, R. M., DAM, R., ZEIGLER, T. R. & NORRIS, L. C. (1959). *J. Nutr.* **68,** 89
LEACH, R. M. & NESHEIM, M. C. (1963). *J. Nutr.* **81,** 193
LEACH, R. M., TURK, D. E., ZEIGLER, T. R. & NORRIS, L. C. (1962). *Poult. Sci.* **41,** 300
LEASE, J. G. (1966). *Poult. Sci.* **45,** 237
LEASE, J. G. & WILLIAMS, W. P. (1967). *Poult. Sci.* **46,** 233
LEPORE, P. W. & MILLER, R. F. (1965). *Proc. Soc. exp. Biol. Med.* **118,** 155
LLOYD, D. R., JENKINS, N. K., COATES, M. E., HARRISON, G. F. & MORRIS, T. R. (1971). *Proc. Nutr. Soc.* **31,** 34A
LONGSTAFF, M. & HILL, R. (1968). *Proc. Nutr. Soc.* **27,** 38A

MCDONALD, M. W. & DILLON, J. F. (1964). *Aust. J. exp. Agric. Anim. Husb.* **4,** 112
MCGHEE, F., CREGER, C. R. & COUCH, J. R. (1965). *Poult. Sci.* **44,** 310
MACINTYRE, T. M., CHANCEY, H. W. R. & GARDINER, E. E. (1963). *Can. J. Anim. Sci.* **43,** 337
MCWARD, G. W. (1967). *Br. Poult. Sci.* **8,** 91
MCWARD, G. W. (1969). *Poult. Sci.* **48,** 791
MCWARD, G. W. & SCOTT, H. M. (1961a). *Poult. Sci.* **40,** 1026
MCWARD, G. W. & SCOTT, H. M. (1961b). *Poult. Sci.* **40,** 1174
MARTIN, W. G. & PATRICK, H. (1961). *Poult. Sci.* **40,** 1004
MATHERS, J. W. & HILL, R. (1967). *Br. J. Nutr.* **21,** 513
MATSUMOTO, T., ITOH, H. & AKIBA, Y. (1968). *Poult. Sci.* **47,** 1323
MEHRING, A. L., BRUMBAUGH, J. H., SUTHERLAND, A. J. & TITUS, H. W. (1960). *Poult. Sci.* **39,** 713
MEHRING, A. L., BRUMBAUGH, J. H. & TITUS, H. W. (1956). *Poult. Sci.* **35,** 956
MILLER, B. F. (1967). *Poult. Sci.* **46,** 686
MILLER, E. C. & DENTON, C. A. (1959). *Poult. Sci.* **38,** 910
MILLER, J. K. & JENSEN, L. S. (1966). *Poult. Sci.* **45,** 1051
MITCHELL, H. H. & EDMAN, M. (1952). *Nutr. Abstr. Rev.* **21,** 787
MOELLER, M. W. & SCOTT, H. M. (1958). *Poult. Sci.* **37,** 1227
MOHAMED, M. S. & GREENBERG, D. M. (1943). *Proc. Soc. exp. Biol. Med.* **54,** 197
MORRIS, B. A. & TAYLOR, T. G. (1967). *Br. Poult. Sci.* **8,** 251
MORRISON, A. B. & SARETT, H. P. (1958). *J. Nutr.* **65,** 267

NEAGLE, L. H., BLAYLOCK, L. G. & GOULD, J. H. (1968). *Poult. Sci.* **47,** 174
NELSON, F. E., JENSEN, L. S. & MCGINNIS, J. (1963). *Poult. Sci.* **42,** 579
NELSON, F. E., LAUBER, J. K. & MIROSH, L. (1964). *Poult. Sci.* **43,** 1346
NELSON, T. S., GILLIS, M. B. & PEELER, H. T. (1962). *Poult. Sci.* **41,** 519
NOTT, H. (1967). Ph.D. thesis, Univ. of Reading
NOTT, H. & COMBS, G. F. (1969). *Poult. Sci.* **48,** 660
NUGARA, D. & EDWARDS, H. M. (1963). *J. Nutr.* **80,** 181

O'DELL, B. L., NEWBERNE, P. M. & SAVAGE, J. E. (1958). *J. Nutr.* **65,** 503
O'DELL, B. L. & SAVAGE, J. E. (1957). *Poult. Sci.* **36,** 459
O'DELL, B. L. & SAVAGE, J. E. (1960). *Proc. Soc. exp. Biol. Med.* **103,** 304
O'DELL, B. L., YOKE, J. M. & SAVAGE, J. E. (1964). *Poult. Sci.* **43,** 415
O'ROURKE, W. F., PHILLIPS, P. H. & CRAVENS, W. W. (1952). *Poult. Sci.* **31,** 962
O'ROURKE, W. F., PHILLIPS, P. H. & CRAVENS, W. W. (1955). *Poult. Sci.* **34,** 47

PAVER, H., ROBERTSON, A. & WILSON, J. E. (1953). *J. comp. Path.* **63,** 31
PENSACK, J. M., HENSON, J. N. & BOGDONOFF, P. D. (1958). *Poult. Sci.* **37,** 1232
PEPPER, W. F., SLINGER, S. J. & MOTZOK, I. (1953). *Poult. Sci.* **32,** 656

PEPPER, W. F., SLINGER, S. J., SUMMERS, J. D. & ASHTON, G. C. (1959). *Can. J. Anim. Sci.* **39**, 182
PETERSEN, C. F., CONRAD, D. H., LUMIJARVI, D. H., SAUTER, E. A. & LAMPMAN, C. E. (1960). *Idaho agric. exp. Stn Res. Bull.* **44**
POLEY, W. E. & MOXON, A. L. (1938). *Poult. Sci.* **17**, 72
POLEY, W. E., WILSON, W. O., MOXON, A. L. & TAYLOR, J. B. (1941). *Poult. Sci.* **20**, 171
POTTER, L. M., LEIGHTON, A. T. & CHU, A. B. (1966). *Poult. Sci.* **45**, 1117
REID, B. L., KURNICK, A. A., SVACHA, R. L. & COUCH, J. R. (1956). *Proc. Soc. exp. Biol. Med.* **93**, 245
ROBERSON, R. H. & SCHAIBLE, P. J. (1958). *Poult. Sci.* **37**, 1321
ROBERSON, R. H. & SCHAIBLE, P. J. (1960a). *Poult. Sci.* **39**, 837
ROBERSON, R. H. & SCHAIBLE, P. J. (1960b). *Poult. Sci.* **39**, 893
ROGLER, J. C., PARKER, H. E., ANDREWS, F. N. & CARRICK, C. W. (1961a). *Poult. Sci.* **40**, 1546
ROGLER, J. C., PARKER, H. E., ANDREWS, F. N. & CARRICK, C. W. (1961b). *Poult. Sci.* **40**, 1554
ROJAS, S. W. & SCOTT, M. L. (1969). *Poult. Sci.* **48**, 819
ROMOSER, G. L., DUDLEY, W. A., MACHLIN, L. J. & LOVELESS, L. (1961). *Poult. Sci.* **40**, 1171
SANFORD, P. E. (1964). *19th Kansas Formula Feed Conference*, 2
SAVAGE, J. E. (1968). *Fedn Proc. Fedn Am. Socs exp. Biol.* **27**, 927
SCHAIBLE, P. J. & BANDEMER, S. L. (1942). *Poult. Sci.* **21**, 8
SCOTT, M. L., BUTTERS, H. E. & RANIT, G. O. (1962). *J. Nutr.* **78**, 223
SCOTT, M. L., HOLM, E. R. & REYNOLDS, R. E. (1958). *Poult. Sci.* **37**, 1419
SCOTT, M. L., HOLM, E. R. & REYNOLDS, R. E. (1959). *Poult. Sci.* **38**, 1344
SCOTT, M. L., VAN TIENHOVEN, A., HOLM, E. R. & REYNOLDS, R. E. (1960). *J. Nutr.* **71**, 282
SELL, J. L. (1965). *Poult. Sci.* **44**, 550
SELYE, H. (1943). *J. Amer. vet. med. Ass.* **103**, 140
SHANE, S. M., YOUNG, R. J. & KROOK, L. (1968). *Proc. Cornell Nutr. Conf.*, 126
SHARMAN, G. A. M. (1960). *Proc. Nutr. Soc.* **19**, 169
SINGSEN, E. P., SPANDORF, A. H., MATTERSON, L. D., SERAFIN, J. A. & TLUSTOHOWICZ, J. J. (1962). *Poult. Sci.* **41**, 1401
SJOLLEMA, B. (1935). *Tierernahrung.* **7**, 184
SMITH, M. S. (1969). *Br. Poult. Sci.* **10**, 97
SULLIVAN, T. W. (1961). *Poult. Sci.* **40**, 334
SULLIVAN, T. W. (1962). *Poult. Sci.* **41**, 1686
SULLIVAN, T. W. (1963). *Poult. Sci.* **42**, 1072
SULLIVAN, T. W. & KINGAN, J. R. (1963). *Poult. Sci.* **42**, 1335
SUPPLEE, W. C. (1964). *Poult. Sci.* **43**, 1599
SUPPLEE, W. C. (1965). *Poult. Sci.* **44**, 1142
SUPPLEE, W. C. (1966). *Poult. Sci.* **45**, 852
SUPPLEE, W. C. & COMBS, G. F. (1960). *Poult. Sci.* **39**, 1211
SUPPLEE, W. C., CREEK, R. D., COMBS, G. F. & BLAMBERG, D. L. (1961). *Poult. Sci.* **40**, 171
SUSO, F. A. & EDWARDS, H. M. (1968a). *Poult. Sci.* **47**, 991
SUSO, F. A. & EDWARDS, H. M. (1968b). *Poult. Sci.* **47**, 1417
SUSO, F. A. & EDWARDS, H. M. (1969). *Poult. Sci.* **48**, 933
TEEKELL, R. A. & WATTS, A. B. (1959). *Poult. Sci.* **38**, 1127
THOMPSON, J. N. & SCOTT, M. L. (1969). *J. Nutr.* **97**, 35
THOMPSON, J. N. & SCOTT, M. L. (1970). *J. Nutr.* **100**, 797
TUPPER, R., WATTS, R. W. E. & WORMALL, A. (1954). *Biochem. J.* **57**, 245
TURK, D. E. & LEASE, J. G. (1962). *Fedn Proc. Fedn Am. Socs exp. Biol.* **21**, 311
TURK, D. E., SUNDE, M. L. & HOEKSTRA, W. G. (1959). *Poult. Sci.* **38**, 1256
TURK, J. L. & KRATZER, F. H. (1960). *Poult. Sci.* **39**, 1302
TWINING, P. F., LILLIE, R. J., ROBEL, E. J. & DENTON, C. A. (1965). *Poult. Sci.* **44**, 283
TYLER, C. & GEAKE, F. H. (1961). *J. Sci. Fd Agric.* **12**, 281
VAN REEN, R. & PEARSON, P. B. (1953). *J. Nutr.* **51**, 191
VOHRA, P. & GONZALES, N. (1969). *Poult. Sci.* **48**, 1509
VOHRA, P. & KRATZER, F. H. (1968a). *Poult. Sci.* **47**, 699

VOHRA, P. & KRATZER, F. H. (1968b). *Poult. Sci.* **47**, 1135
WADDELL, D. G. & SELL, J. L. (1964). *Poult. Sci.* **43**, 1249
WAIBEL, P. E., SNETSINGER, D. C., BALL, R. A. & SAUTER, J. H. (1964). *Poult. Sci.* **43**, 504
WALDROUP, P. W., AMMERMAN, C. B. & HARMS, R. H. (1962). *Poult. Sci.* **41**, 1433
WALDROUP, P. W., AMMERMAN, C. B. & HARMS, R. H. (1965). *Poult. Sci.* **44**, 1302
WALDROUP, P. W., STEARNS, J. E., AMMERMAN, C. B. & HARMS, R. H. (1965). *Poult. Sci.* **44**, 543
WALTER, E. D. & AITKEN, J. R. (1962). *Poult. Sci.* **41**, 386
WALTER, E. D. & JENSEN, L. S. (1963). *J. Nutr.* **80**, 327
WALTER, E. D. & JENSEN, L. S. (1964). *Poult. Sci.* **43**, 919
WATSON, L. T., AMMERMAN, C. B., MILLER, S. M. & HARMS, R. H. (1970). *Poult. Sci.* **49**, 1548
WEBER, C. W., DOBERENZ, A. R. & REID, B. L. (1969). *Poult. Sci.* **48**, 230
WHITE-STEVENS, R. H., PENSACK, J. M. & STOKSTAD, E. L. R. (1960). *Poult. Sci.* **39**. 1305
WILCOX, R. A., CARLSON, C. W., KOHLMEYER, W. & GASTLER, G. F. (1961). *Poult. Sci.* **40**, 94
WILGUS, H. S., GASSNER, F. X., PATTON, A. R. & HARSHFIELD, G. S. (1948). *Poult. Sci.* **27**, 686
WILGUS, H. S., NORRIS, L. C. & HEUSER, G. F. (1937a). *Poult. Sci.* **16**, 232
WILGUS, H. S., NORRIS, L. C. & HEUSER, G. F. (1937b). *Poult. Sci.* **16**, 155
WILSON, H. R., PERSONS, J. N., ROWLAND, L. O. & HARMS, R. H. (1969). *Poult. Sci.* **48**, 798
WOERPEL, H. R. & BALLOUN, S. L. (1964). *Poult. Sci.* **43**, 1134
WRIGHT, P. L. & MRAZ, F. R. (1964). *Poult. Sci.* **43**, 947
YOUNG, R. J., EDWARDS, H. M. & GILLIS, M. B. (1958). *Poult. Sci.* **37**, 1100
ZEIGLER, T. R., LEACH, R. M., NORRIS, L. C. & SCOTT, M. L. (1961). *Poult. Sci.* **40**, 1584

CHAPTER 4

REQUIREMENTS FOR VITAMINS, CHOLINE AND
ESSENTIAL FATTY ACIDS

INTRODUCTION

The tables of estimates of vitamin requirements of poultry have been compiled from information published in Europe and the USA throughout the last thirty years. Where more than two estimates were available the median value has been given, together with the range over which it was calculated. An attempt has been made in each instance to determine the least quantity of a vitamin that must be given in the diet to prevent signs of deficiency and to satisfy exactly the bird's need for optimal performance within its class, i.e. for maximal growth, egg production or fertility. Where possible the selected values have been taken from experiments in which defined diets of purified ingredients were used. By this means a new assessment, based largely on modern work, has replaced the former values for some vitamins. For others, no recent quantitative investigations appear to have been made and it has been impossible to qualify the previous values. "Optimal performance" has been taken to imply reasonable stores of the vitamin in the egg or tissues. In view of the known carry-over of some vitamins from the hen to her chicks, experiments have been disregarded if the level of supplementation of the hen's diet seemed excessive. Investigations in which the criteria of adequacy included more-than-average stores of a vitamin in the eggs, or in the tissues of the hatched chick, have also been ignored.

No allowances have been made to cover losses during preparation and storage of the diets. The need for such allowances will depend on the stability of each particular vitamin, which in turn will be affected by factors such as the form in which it is present, interactions with other ingredients of the diet, and the temperature attained during pelleting and storage; but the subject is too complicated to be adequately treated here.

Requirements have been stated in terms of an amount per unit weight of air-dry diet, rather than as a daily allowance. The former is the customary method of expression, and is probably the most valid biologically. Since vitamins are intimately involved in the metabolism of nutrients, the demand for them may reasonably be expected to be related to the amount of food eaten. It must be noted, however, that the weight of food eaten may be inversely proportional to its content of metabolizable energy. There have been a few attempts, cited in the text, to determine the effect of dietary energy content on the quantitative requirements of poultry for vitamins, but information is sparse. In general, the recorded values have been obtained from experiments in which the ME content of the diets was between 2·8 and 3·1 Mcal/kg (11·7 to 13·0 MJ/kg). In diets of markedly higher ME content it might be advisable to increase the vitamin levels proportionately. However, the margin of uncertainty involved in measuring the requirement for a vitamin is usually much wider than the adjustment that would be needed to allow for differences in dietary energy concentration.

Other factors that may have a general effect on vitamin requirements are breed and management. There have been a few investigations of possible differences in requirements for particular vitamins between different breeds of fowl, but there is not enough evidence to draw any general conclusions. Management may influence the need for a dietary source of some vitamins because of their synthesis by micro-organisms in the alimentary tract. It is known that vitamins of the B complex and vitamin K are produced by microbial action in the gut, and there is some evidence that the extent of synthesis may be influenced by the carbohydrate composition of the diet. However, these products of microbial synthesis seem largely unavailable to the bird unless it has access to its excreta, and hence only birds maintained on free range or deep litter are likely to derive any significant contribution to their dietary vitamin requirement from this source.

VITAMIN A

EFFECTS OF DEPRIVATION

In young birds the clinical signs of a lack of vitamin A are poor growth and feather formation, unco-ordinated movement (ataxia), keratinization of the mucous membranes characterised by lesions round the eyes and mouth, and an increased susceptibility to infection. In severe cases death occurs within a few weeks. Deposits of urates in the kidney tubules and ureters are a frequent post mortem finding. Donovan (1965b) observed a tendency to longer and heavier small intestines in chicks given diets low in vitamin A. Other anatomical abnormalities that have been associated with the deficiency in growing birds are reduced bursa weights and heavier adrenals and testes (Nockels and Kienholz, 1966, 1967).

In adult birds the deficiency is characterised by loss of condition accompanied by ataxia, keratinized membranes and renal gout. Egg production dwindles and finally ceases. An increased incidence of blood spots has been recorded in eggs from hens given inadequate vitamin A (Bearse, McClary and Saxena, 1960). In the male, Paredes and Garcia (1959) observed a decrease in fertility, with a reduction in sperm count and motility.

Until recently it has been impossible to demonstrate severe deficiency of vitamin A in chick embryos because hens deprived of it fail to lay eggs. However, it has now been shown that retinoic acid can replace true vitamin A for growth, egg production and prevention of nervous lesions (Thompson, Howell, Pitt and Houghton, 1965). Eggs from hens maintained on a dietary supplement of methyl retinoate develop normally only for the first 48 hours of incubation. Older embryos show a gradual disintegration, characterised particularly by a failure to develop an organised circulatory system. Thus it appears that the developing embryo is extremely sensitive to a lack of true vitamin A.

The replacement of secretory epithelia by keratinized membranes is a likely cause of the increased susceptibility to infection in birds lacking vitamin A. This may be particularly true of intestinal parasitic infestation (see review by Randall, 1964). Vitamin A may also play a more fundamental role in disease resistance since there are indications that its deficiency may lead to impaired production of antibodies (Leutskaja, 1963; Panda and Combs, 1963).

ASSESSMENT OF REQUIREMENT

In young birds the need for vitamin A can be said to be satisfied if there are no clinical signs of deficiency and if growth rate and general condition cannot be improved by higher amounts. It is questionable whether allowance should also be made for storage in the liver. Deposition of small quantities in the liver is indicative that the bird is in positive vitamin A balance, and several workers have included "moderate liver stores" among their criteria of adequacy. For the purpose of the present assessment, no account has been taken of experiments in which high deposits in the liver have been used as a measure of requirement.

In laying hens the maintenance of egg production is the essential criterion and, for table eggs, there is no particular advantage in high yolk stores of vitamin A. If the eggs are to be used for hatching, they must be endowed with enough of the vitamin to carry the embryo through to hatching and to supply some reserve for the newly hatched chick.

Previous estimates of the requirement of poultry for vitamin A have been largely based on early work in which the source of vitamin A was the preformed vitamin, frequently in the form of fish liver oils or their concentrates, or its carotenoid precursors. It is well known that vitamin A is prone to oxidative destruction, not only during the course of preparation and storage of diets but also in the tissue of the animal to which it is fed. β-carotene is more stable but its availability to the bird may be adversely affected by a variety of factors so that, in practice, its theoretical vitamin A value of half that of the preformed vitamin may be a gross over-estimate.

In recent years "stabilized" vitamin A preparations have been developed for use in animal feeds. They take the form of dry powders in which the vitamin A is finely dispersed in a protective coating, with or without addition of an anti-oxidant. This type of preparation has been shown to compare favourably with oily solutions or β-carotene in availability and biological activity for poultry (Ascarelli, 1957; Olsen, Harvey, Hill and Branion, 1959a; Brubacher, Gloor, Wiss, Würsch and Tagwerker, 1962; Tiews and Kring, 1962). In arriving at the present estimate of the vitamin A requirements of poultry account has been taken only of experiments in which stabilized forms of vitamin A were used, since their results are less likely to be vitiated by indeterminate losses from the food before it is eaten by the bird.

Table 4.1
Estimates of the vitamin A requirement of the young growing chick using stabilized vitamin A palmitate or acetate

Source	Criteria of adequacy	Breed of chick	Estimated requirement (i.u./kg diet)
Hill, Scott, Norris & Heuser (1961)	Growth and survival to 4 weeks	White Leghorn	1320
Olsen, Hill & Branion (1964)	Growth and survival to 4 weeks; moderate liver stores	Columbian Rock and New Hampshire	1320
Donovan (1965a)	Per cent average daily gains from 14 to 32 days	Whited Leghorn White Plymouth Rock White Mountain	1732 1111 832
Wilson & Teekell (1966)	Satisfactory growth to 5 weeks with negligible liver stores	(not stated)	1100

Most evidence is available for the growing chick, and several breeds have been investigated. Table 4.1 gives the details of six estimations, from which the median value of 1320 i.u./kg has been derived. Several other papers lend support to this figure although the data given do not permit precise quantitative assessment. Thus Kurnick, Heywang, Hullett, Vavich and Reid (1964) reported only small, non-significant increases in growth of WL pullet chicks given supplements of vitamin A greater than 1250 i.u./kg; Thornton and Whittet (1962)

95

found that vitamin A levels ranging from 1760 to 6600 i.u./kg did not improve the growth rate or feed efficiency of SCWL chicks, and in an abstract in which full experimental details were not given Singh and Donovan (1966) calculated the requirement of White Mountain crossbred chicks to be approximately 1550 i.u./kg.

Information on the vitamin A requirements of other classes of poultry is sparse. Two groups of workers are in close agreement regarding the requirement of SCWL layers, and as the level of vitamin A needed for maximal egg production also sustained fertility and the hatchability of fertile eggs, it can be assumed adequate for breeding hens as well. The two values given for breeding turkeys are also in good agreement. Only one fully documented investigation has been found on the vitamin A requirement for turkey poults. Stoewsand and Scott (1961a) considered 1760 i.u./kg adequate for optimal food utilization and growth to eight weeks, although they pointed out that a much higher amount (5280 i.u./kg) was needed to ensure minimal blood levels of uric acid and appreciable liver stores of the vitamin. A brief report of Chavez, Creger and Couch (1963) also recommends a higher level (4400 i.u./kg) for growth and liver storage.

UTILIZATION OF CAROTENOIDS

The carotenoids, which occur naturally in green leaves and yellow maize, are precursors of vitamin A. Since conversion of the provitamin to vitamin A takes place mainly in the small intestine, the carotenoids are only effective if given by mouth. By far the most active precursor is β-carotene, one molecule of which gives rise to one molecule of vitamin A, so that theoretically, on a weight for weight basis, it has half the biological activity of preformed vitamin A. The international unit is defined in terms of either substance, being the activity contained in 0·3 μg vitamin A alcohol or 0·6 μg β-carotene. In practice, however, the theoretical value is seldom achieved and, among the many investigations into the value of β-carotene for poultry, evidence can be found for a biological activity superior, equal or inferior to that of vitamin A. Earlier work on the subject has been reviewed by Marusich and Bauernfeind (1963) and Olsen, Hill and Brannion (1964). The relative efficiency of dietary vitamin A and carotenoids is determined by a combination of their respective stability, both in the diet and in the digestive tract, and utilization by the bird. Some of the evidence in favour of β-carotene may be a reflection of its greater stability, particularly when it has been compared with vitamin A in fish liver oils. Evidence on the relative utilization of the two substances is likely to be more valid if based on comparisons with stabilized forms of vitamin A. Data from such comparisons are given in Table 4.2, In a direct comparison in growing chicks of vitamin A and β-carotene, both given in the form of stabilized gelatin beadlets, Marusich and Bauernfeind (1963) concluded that, at levels near to the physiological requirement for growth, the two substances were unit for unit equally effective. At high levels intended to produce appreciable liver stores vitamin A was two and a half to four times more effective. Their finding of equivalence at the lower level was supported by Parrish, Zimmerman, Sanford and Hung (1963), and the greater efficiency of vitamin A in promoting liver storage at higher doses was confirmed by Ely (1959). However, Gledhill and Smith (1955) and Olsen et al. (1964) both found the preformed vitamin more effective, even at levels close to the requirements for growth. In WL hens Krieg (1963) also found that at high levels of supplementation vitamin A promoted greater liver stores than β-carotene in crystalline form or as lucerne; eggs from birds given carotene or alfalfa had a deeper colour but were similar in vitamin A content to those from hens given the preformed vitamin. In practical terms, therefore, particularly

96

Table 4.2
Estimates of the biological value for chicks of β-carotene as a source of vitamin A

Source	Form of vitamin A	Form of β-carotene	Levels tested (i.u./kg diet)	Criteria of response	Amount (i.u.) of β-carotene equivalent to 1 i.u. vitamin A
Gledhill & Smith (1955)	Stabilized dry carrier	Alfalfa	1100 and 2200	Growth, feed efficiency, survival, liver storage	Alfalfa less effective
	Fish liver oil or palmitate in oil	Alfalfa and maize meal	10 560	Liver storage	1·3
Ely (1959)	Wax coated dry carrier	Alfalfa and maize meal	10 560	Liver storage	2·6
Marusich & Bauernfeind (1963)	Stabilized gelatin beadlets	Stabilized gelatin beadlets	4400 to 22 000	Liver storage	2·5 to 4
		Alfalfa	1100	Liver storage	1
			550 to 11 000	Liver storage	2·5 to 4
Parrish, Zimmerman, Sanford & Hung (1963)	ANRC dry reference preparation and USP reference oil	Alfalfa	880 and 1760	Growth, blood level, liver storage	1
Olsen, Hill & Branion (1964)	Stabilized gelatin beadlets	Crystalline β-carotene	660 to 2640	Liver storage	β-carotene effective

if liver storage of vitamin A is desirable, it seems wise to supply β-carotene in more liberal amounts than the calculated equivalent of preformed vitamin A.

Ascarelli and Bondi (1957), in a study of the utilization by young chicks of carotene from different plant sources, showed that although the chick is capable of satisfying its vitamin A requirement for growth and liver storage from forage plants, nevertheless the biological value of carotene from different kinds of forage varied considerably. They recommended that green plants should be given freely if they were to be used as a source of vitamin A.

There is evidence that high doses of vitamin A interefere with the utilization of β-carotene. Levels of 13 200 i.u./kg diet suppressed pigmentation and carotenoid levels in serum and liver of broiler chicks (Dua and Day, 1964; Dua, Tipon and Day, 1965). Total carotenoids in serum and egg yolks of SCWL hens decreased with increasing level of dietary vitamin A palmitate in excess of 110 000 i.u./kg (Gutzmann and Donovan, 1966). Although this fact is unimportant in the nutrition of the bird it may be of significance in terms of carcass or egg quality.

EFFECTS OF EXCESS VITAMIN A

Overdosage with vitamin A can lead to toxicosis, but a dose many times the recommended dietary level is necessary to provoke serious consequences. The most frequently observed clinical signs of hypervitaminosis A in young chicks include loss of appetite, decreased growth rate, diarrhoea, encrustations around the mouth and reddening of the eyelids (Wolbach and Hegsted, 1952; Pudelkiewicz, Webster, Olsen and Matterson, 1964; Tiews and Zentz, 1967a, b; Baker, Howell and Thompson 1967; Taylor, Morris and Kirkley, 1968). In ducklings given vitamin A supplements up to 600 000 i.u. daily for 22 days, Wolbach and Hegsted (1952) observed no adverse effects other than decreased feed intake leading to slower rate of growth. There have been a few investigations in older birds. Biely, Wood and Topliff (1962) reported a marked drop in egg production by hens given about 1 000 000 i.u. vitamin A/kg diet. A consistent decline in egg production was also noted by Donovan, Henderson and Luneau (1961) after hens had been fed for three weeks a diet containing 242 000 i.u./kg. Eggs from these birds had a greater incidence of meat and blood spots than those from hens given more moderate levels of the vitamin.

Skeletal defects and anaemia, both characteristic of vitamin A excess in rats, have not been consistently observed in birds. The original report of Wolbach and Hegsted (1952) of bone lesions in chicks given large doses of vitamin A was confirmed by Baker et al. (1967), although they disagreed with respect to the details of the abnormalities. None of the other investigators observed any deleterious effect of hypervitaminosis on bone development. There appears to be a threshold in liver storage of vitamin A. Pudelkiewicz et al. (1964) found no increase in liver stores with doses in excess of 500 mg vitamin A acetate/kg nor could Tiews and Zentz (1967b) find any relation between toxicosis and deposits of vitamin A in the liver.

According to Tiews and Zentz (1967b) the subacute toxic threshold for chicks was reached by a daily intake of 65 mg (214 500 i.u.) vitamin A/kg body weight, but they suggest that chronic toxicity may result from smaller quantities. They found that 400 mg/kg feed were tolerated for 40 days, but thereafter gave rise to toxic effects. In the experience of Pudelkiewicz et al. (1964) higher levels were tolerated; no adverse effects were apparent at an intake of 220 000 i.u./kg body weight, but five times that quantity depressed feed intake within 24 h of administration. Taylor et al. (1968) only observed signs of toxicity when the level in the diet reached 2 600 000 i.u./kg. These conflicting reports make it impossible to quote a precise level above which vitamin A becomes toxic but it is clear that, in chicks, hypervitaminosis A is not likely to be encountered under ordinary feeding conditions. In laying hens there may be greater need for caution, in view of the report of March and Biely (1964) that a moderately excessive level of vitamin A (22 000 i.u./kg diet) caused a decline in egg production from 65·8% to 60·8% in White Leghorn pullets over a twelve week period. The decline was not evident when the greater part of the vitamin A was supplied in the form of carotene in dried cereal grass. Conversely Mehner, Torges and Vogt (1965) found 64 000 i.u. vitamin A/kg diet to have no influence on laying rate, egg weight or egg quality in an experiment lasting 10 weeks. These workers, and also Donovan et al. (1961), noted a decrease in yolk colour with high intakes of vitamin A. These observations provide further evidence that high doses of vitamin A interfere with utilization of carotenoids.

FACTORS AFFECTING THE REQUIREMENT FOR VITAMIN A

Genetic effects

A few attempts have been made to compare directly the requirements for vitamin A of chicks from standard laying breeds with those of the faster growing broiler strains. Thornton and Whittet (1962) could find no difference in growth or feed efficiency between male and female White Leghorn or New Hampshire × Delaware chicks given dietary levels of vitamin A over the range of 1760 to 7000 i.u./kg. This evidence is, however, of limited value since the lowest level of vitamin A was apparently above the minimal requirements for either breed. Olsen, Hill and Brannion (1964) compared the utilization of vitamin A and carotene by two strains of Columbian Rocks and one of New Hampshire chicks in terms of weight gain, survival and liver storage. The vitamin supplements ranged from 660 to 2640 i.u./kg diet. They found differences in liver stores, which were highest in the New Hampshires, and in final body weights, which were least in one of the strains of Columbian Rocks. In spite of these differences there was no indication that breed or strain affected requirement, although the authors suggest that their levels of vitamin A may not have been suitably spaced to detect relatively small differences in requirement. Donovan (1965a) investigated early growth and liver stores of slow and fast growing breeds given vitamin A supplements from 220 to 7040 i.u./kg diet. Growth was assessed in terms of percent relative average daily gains, and requirement was estimated by a least squares procedure. Donovan concluded that, whether the assessment was made as i.u./kg diet or as daily intake/kg body weight, White Mountain chicks, which achieved the greatest weight, had the lowest requirement. The slow growing White Leghorn chicks were said to require about twice as much vitamin A as the White Mountain chicks, and White Plymouth Rocks were intermediate. The faster growing birds consumed more feed, and hence more vitamin A, during the experimental period, but their intake of the vitamin per unit weight was nevertheless much the same as that of the slower growing birds. Thus their lower dietary requirement could not be related to feed intake but was a reflection of a reduced metabolic need for vitamin A. Liver storage was not affected by breed. Deficiency of vitamin A seemed to be more detrimental to the two broiler strains than to the White Leghorns. This work needs confirmation from other investigators before it can be fully accepted, but if it is established that, in general, the requirement of fast growing strains for vitamin A is reduced, the value given in the table of requirements is likely to be somewhat generous for broiler strains.

Other dietary constituents

It has been shown in several species of livestock that utilization of vitamin A and carotene is improved by addition of fat to the diet (see reviews by Siedler, Enzer and Schweigert, 1956, and Denton and Bielanski, 1958). In experiments with Columbian Rock chicks to four weeks of age, Olsen, Harvey, Hill and Branion (1959b) investigated the effects of varying the energy and protein levels of the diet on utilization of vitamin A and carotene; liver storage was their criterion of response. Increasing the level of dietary energy led to increased liver stores of vitamin A, but as the extra energy was supplied in the form of lard it is not clear whether higher energy *per se* or higher fat content was responsible for the better storage. Thornton and Whittet (1962) made a direct attempt to measure the effect of the dietary level and source of energy on the vitamin A requirements of different breeds of chick. However, the lowest level of vitamin A tested (1760 i.u./kg) satisfied requirements on all diets, and there was thus no indication that the source of energy or its level in the diet influenced the chick's need for vitamin A. The values quoted in Table 4.1 are based on work with diets ranging from 3·1 to 3·7 Mcal (13·0 to 15·5 MJ) ME/kg. Within these limits we have no evidence of a correlation between energy content of the diet and the chick's requirement for vitamin A. However, there is a need for further investigation of this question with trials which include levels of vitamin A below the recommended minimum.

There are strong indications from work with mammalian species that the metabolism of vitamin A is affected by the dietary protein level. In the experiments quoted above, Olsen *et al.* (1959b) studied the effects of varying the amount of protein, keeping dietary energy constant. Their findings showed an inverse relation between dietary protein level and storage of vitamin A in the liver, which led them to suggest that requirements for the vitamin may be greater at high protein intakes. Decreased liver stores with high protein diets were also reported by Stoewsand and Scott (1964a). They further showed that the high protein diets induced hyperactivity of the adrenal cortex, and postulated that the resulting increase in production of corticosterone might be responsible for mobilizing vitamin A from the liver as part of the bird's defence against "stress" (Stoewsand and Scott, 1964b). In a series of investigations with low protein diets Nir and Ascarelli (1966, 1967a, b) found the rate of depletion of liver stores of vitamin A was decreased on diets containing 50 g protein/kg. This, however, appeared to be due to a failure to mobilize the reserves in the liver; the inadequate protein intake led to changes in plasma proteins and consequent impairment of the mechanism of transport of vitamin A. Thus in some instances of malnutrition liver stores may not be a true indication of the bird's vitamin A status since, unless these reserves can be mobilized, they are of little value. Nir and Ascarelli (1967b) failed to confirm an earlier finding by Stoewsand and Scott (1961b) that restriction of protein intake increased the survival time of chicks deprived of vitamin A.

Disease

The increased susceptibility to infection of birds deprived of vitamin A raises questions regarding the extent to which requirement for vitamin A may be increased in diseased birds, and whether or not high doses can protect against initial infection or influence its clinical course. The relation between coccidiosis and vitamin A nutrition has been the subject of considerable study; other common diseases of poultry have received less attention in this respect.

Earlier indications that chicks with a marginal intake of vitamin A were more susceptible to coccidiosis have recently been re-examined. Erasmus, Scott and

Levine (1960) reported that, after infection with *Eimeria tenella* and *E. acervulina*, chicks receiving 17 600 i.u. vitamin A/kg diet regained appetite and grew faster than those given only 1760 i.u./kg. The infected birds stored less of the vitamin in their livers. The severity of the disease was similar whatever the level of vitamin A, but recovery of the surviving birds was improved with increasing doses of the vitamin. β-carotene was less effective in this respect. Panda, Combs and DeVolt (1964) also observed a small but significant lowering of liver reserves in birds infected with *E. acervulina* and *E. necatrix*. During the acute phase of a moderately severe infection chicks given 2645 i.u./kg diet gained less weight than others given three or nine times that amount, but the later course of the disease was not affected by the dietary vitamin A level. Singh and Donovan (1966) calculated that the requirement of vitamin A for optimal growth increased from about 1550 to 2650 i.u./kg diet in chicks inoculated with *E. acervulina* or *E. necatrix*. In a spontaneous outbreak of coccidiosis Gerriets (1961) observed that chicks given 5000 i.u. vitamin A/kg feed suffered a much smaller mortality than birds deprived of vitamin A. Coles, Biely and March (1970) also reported more severe effects of *E. acervulina* infection in chicks with a suboptimal intake of vitamin A. In further experiments Gerriets deliberately exposed chicks to infection and reported that losses due to coccidiosis were inversely related to the amounts of vitamin A in the diet. In later studies (Gerriets, 1966) it was claimed that in the large-scale rearing of pullets 30 000 i.u. vitamin A/kg feed reduced mortality rate and gave better protection against coccidiosis than did 80 mg/kg Zoalene (3,5-dinitro-o-toluamide, Dow Chemical Company, Midland, Michigan). However, at lower levels of vitamin A (up to 3800 i.u./kg) Waldroup, Simpson, Cox and Harms (1963) failed to influence morbidity or mortality of chicks experimentally infected with *E. tenella*.

In turkeys challenged with *Heterakis gallinarum*, mortality tended to be less with increasing vitamin A level in the diet from none to 3400 i.u./kg (Whitmore, Sullivan and Grace, 1966). In a study of poultry kept under field conditions in India, Pande and Krishnamurty (1959) reported that hypovitaminosis A and ascaridiasis accounted for more than half the mortality in the flock. A lack of vitamin A favoured infestation with *Ascaridia galli* and this in turn exacerbated deficiency of the vitamin, presumably because of damage to the intestinal mucosa and consequently impaired ability to convert β-carotene or absorb vitamin A. Liver stores of the vitamin were lower in the infested birds. When vitamin A was provided in the form of 50 g green feed daily the birds remained reasonably healthy on ground contaminated with ova of *Ascaridia galli*.

In non-parasitic infections there is less evidence of beneficial effects from high doses of vitamin A. Boyd and Edwards (1962) did not find lowered liver reserves of vitamin A in chicks infected with *Mycoplasma gallisepticum*, indicating that the infection had not interfered with absorption or metabolism of the vitamin. Mortality was greatest among infected birds totally deprived of vitamin A, but with supplements of 110 to 7040 i.u./kg diet there was no difference in survival rate between infected and uninfected birds. In breeding turkeys naturally infected with *Mycoplasma* the highest incidence of air-sac lesions was observed in embryos from dams severely depleted of vitamin A (Abbot, McMartin, Adler and Kratzer, 1960), but it was not possible to determine whether high levels in the parental diet had any therapeutic effect. In naturally-occurring infections of Newcastle disease total serum proteins, vitamin A and carotenoids were depressed (Squibb, Braham, Guzham and Scrimshaw, 1955). In later studies with experimentally infected chicks Squibb and Veros (1961) found that in birds with adequate body reserves of vitamin A, no benefit resulted from vitamin A therapy, even with doses as high as 110 000 i.u./kg diet. At inadequate vitamin A intake, however, there was greater mortality from the combined effects of infection and avitaminosis than from either alone. In one study of lymphomatosis Krieg and Löliger (1963) showed that, on a proprietary feed containing at least 11 000 i.u. vitamin A/kg, healthy chicks stored more vitamin A in their livers than others in which the disease had been experimentally induced. They postulated that the infection might have interfered with bile production and hence with absorption of vitamin A. However, high dietary supplements of vitamin A do not influence the susceptibility or resistance of chicks to agents of the avian leucosis complex (Mitrovic, Marusich and Deutsch, 1969).

From these results there is no clear indication of generalised increase in requirement for vitamin A by diseased birds. In certain diseases, as for example parasitic infestations which damage the mucosa of the digestive tract, absorption of vitamin A may be impaired and an increased level in the diet is perhaps advisable, particularly if high liver stores or deposits in the egg are desired. Since vitamin A is concerned in maintaining the integrity of the mucosa and, possibly, in the production of antibodies, it is essential that the requirement for these functions should be satisfactorily met if the bird is to withstand infection. There is, however, little to indicate that doses greatly in excess of the recommended level are of prophylactic or therapeutic value.

Temperature studies

Some effort has been made by workers in hot climates to detect whether or not the vitamin A requirements of birds kept under such conditions are satisfied by the recommended dietary levels. Heywang (1952) found that laying and breeding hens needed higher levels of vitamin A in the diet in hot than in cool weather to maintain egg production and hatchability. However, as feed intake was depressed in hot weather his finding does not necessarily imply a higher physiological requirement. In acute experiments in which hens were exposed to high ambient temperatures for a few days, their blood levels after a single oral dose of vitamin A were not significantly lower than those of control birds maintained in a cooler environment (Squibb, Braham and Arroyave, 1958). Ascarelli and Bartov (1963) gave oral doses of vitamin A to chicks reared in normal and moderately elevated temperatures. Although there was poorer growth in the warmer environment, there was no decrease in liver or plasma vitamin A, nor any effect on survival time. They concluded that they had no evidence for increased vitamin A requirement in a hot climate. In an extensive study with pullet chicks reared to 10 or 20 weeks of age in a hot arid climate Kurnick, Heywang, Hulett, Vavich and Reid (1964) also failed to establish an increase in requirement for vitamin A. The chicks raised during the cooler months had higher liver stores, but this again might have been accounted for by a higher feed intake. In general, therefore, there seems little indication that high environmental temperatures affect the bird's need for vitamin A, although if the requirement is calculated as a level in the diet it may have to be increased in environmental temperatures which depress feed consumption.

The relation between vitamin intake and cold stress was examined by Scholtyssek (1963). Battery hens were exposed to chilling at intervals throughout the experimental period of 180 days. The effects of the stress, as judged by the number of birds that moulted, was mitigated by a supplement of vitamins A (60 000 i.u.), D_3 (6000 i.u.), E (30 mg) and C (300 mg) given three weeks after each period of stress. The supplement was ineffective, even in increased amounts, if given prior to the stress. No experiments were done with each vitamin separately and hence it is not certain whether vitamin A contributed to the beneficial effect of the treatment.

VITAMIN D

FORMS OF VITAMIN D

Several irradiated sterols have vitamin D activity for birds and mammals. The most important are vitamin D_2 (ergocalciferol) and vitamin D_3 (cholecalciferol). Both are equally effective in most mammals, but for birds vitamin D_2 is much less potent as an antirachitic agent. Earlier workers have suggested a ratio of activity for chicks of vitamin D_3 to vitamin D_2 of about 35:1 (Remp and Marshall, 1938; McChesney, 1943). This has been recently confirmed by Gunther and Tekin (1964) who assessed the relative potencies in terms of weight gain of chicks at 42:1 on a diet with a Ca:P ratio of 3:1. However, Chen and Bosmann (1964) found vitamin D_3 only eight to eleven times as effective as vitamin D_2 in increasing serum levels of Ca and P in rachitic chicks. In the following paragraphs, vitamin D should be taken to mean, unless otherwise specified, cholecalciferol.

EFFECTS OF DEPRIVATION

In animals and bird vitamin D is formed by the action of ultra-violet radiation on precursors of the vitamin in the superficial tissues. Thus the amount required in the diet depends on the extent of exposure to sunlight and, in poultry, gross signs of deficiency are usually only encountered under conditions of indoor management. In young birds deprivation of vitamin D results in rickets; the skeleton is not properly calcified, the bones are shortened and deformed. The condition is usually accompanied by an increase in plasma alkaline phosphatase, which Motzok (1950) has shown to be inversely related to the dietary level of vitamin D. Body weight is below normal, largely as a result of retarded skeletal growth. In certain breeds an abnormal blackening of the feathers has been observed (Glazener, Mattingly and Briggs, 1946; Glazener and Briggs, 1948). Changes in the enzyme activities and amino acid composition of the cartilage have been reported (Cipera and Willmer, 1963; Cipera, 1967). In adults osteomalacia develops, as a result of loss of calcium from the skeleton. Egg production is depressed and shell quality deteriorates. Hertelendy and Taylor (1965) showed that response to oestrogens was decreased in cocks deprived of vitamin D, and suggested that a reduced ability to synthesize yolk proteins in hens may be a factor in the decline in egg production. A reduction in size of oviducts and ova, and slight enlargement of adrenals and parathyroids, has been reported (Turk and McGinnis, 1964). Abnormalities in embryos from hens depleted of vitamin D include early anaemia, generalised oedema and shortened and bent hind limbs (Karb, 1967).

ASSESSMENT OF REQUIREMENT

Most estimates of adequacy of vitamin D in chicks have been based on maintenance of both normal growth and bone mineral content (usually assessed after reducing the tibias to ash). According to Waldroup, Ammerman and Harms (1963) bone ash is the more sensitive measure, but the two responses are usually well correlated.

There is a close interrelationship between vitamin D, calcium and phosphorus, and it is not possible to state a requirement for the vitamin without reference to the dietary content of Ca and P (see also Chapter 3). Table 4.3 summarises estimates from a number of laboratories of the vitamin D requirement of growing chicks given diets with different levels of calcium and phosphorus. The values marked with an asterisk have been obtained with diets containing roughly the recommended levels of both minerals, i.e. from 7 to 10 g Ca/kg, 6·5 to 7·0 g

P/kg, and a Ca:P ratio of between 1·0 and 1·8:1·0. From these the median value of 400 i.u./kg diet has been derived and is given as the requirement in Table 4.5. From the data in Table 4.3 it is generally evident that the requirement for vitamin D increases as the level of calcium falls, and is least when calcium and phosphorus levels are optimal. There is also evidence that the form, as well as the quantity, of dietary phosphorus may affect the requirement for vitamin D, but the question of phosphorus availability is dealt with in Chapter 3.

There has been little recent work on the quantitative requirements of laying or breeding hens for vitamin D, and the previous estimates have not been modified. The criteria on which the estimates were based included fertility, hatchability and shell quality as well as egg production, hence the estimate of 600 i.u./kg is likely to be adequate for breeders as well as layers. A brief note by Walsh, Kingan and Sullivan (1963), who obtained satisfactory egg production with 25 g Ca and 340 i.u. vitamin D/kg diet, suggests that the requirement for layers may in fact be slightly lower.

The previous estimate for the requirement of turkey poults (1100 i.u./kg) was calculated from nine values found in the literature up to 1950. At the time the work was done there was no international standard for vitamin D_3 and requirements for poultry were expressed in units represented by reference cod liver oils. Two more modern studies, using vitamin D_3 assayed in terms of the present international standard, indicate a slightly lower requirement. Sullivan and Kingan (1963) considered that Broad Breasted Bronze turkey poults required a minimum of 900 i.u./kg in diets containing at least 5 g available P/kg. Neagle, Blaylock and Goihl (1968) suggested that between 550 and 1100 i.u./kg, with 12 g Ca and 8 g P/kg, was adequate for maximum performance to 4 weeks of age. In view of a slight ambiguity regarding the potency of earlier standards, the more recent estimate of 900 i.u./kg is preferred. In the absence of more recent estimates of requirements for other classes of poultry the previous estimates have been used.

TOXICITY OF VITAMIN D

Gross toxic effects of vitamin D have been observed in man and laboratory mammals with doses many hundreds of times in excess of normal requirements (Deuel, 1957), but even on lower doses some harm can result. Hypervitaminosis D can also occur in birds, although there is little direct evidence to indicate a safe level of administration. Chen and Bosmann (1965) noted some depression of growth after 27 days in chicks given 40 000 i.u. vitamin D_3 daily; vitamin D_2 was only about one tenth as toxic. Griminger (1966b) observed no depression of fertility or hatchability in Leghorn hens and cocks given 60 000 i.u. vitamin D_3/kg diet; the progeny from these birds apparently carried over sufficient stores of vitamin D to support relatively good growth for 5 weeks. Taylor, Morris and Kirkley (1968) observed an increase in Ca and a decrease in inorganic P in the plasma of chicks given 500 000 i.u. vitamin D_3/kg diet, but no adverse signs with 50 000 i.u./kg. Thus it appears that doses in excess of 100 times the requirement of vitamin D are tolerated without detrimental effects.

FACTORS AFFECTING THE REQUIREMENT FOR VITAMIN D

Several natural foods including hay, fresh green cereals and yeast have been shown to have rachitogenic properties for mammals but it is not known whether they have a similar effect in poultry. Coates and Harrison (1957) found that uncooked pig's liver was rachitogenic for chicks; about 20 g raw liver counteracted the effect of 3 i.u. vitamin D_3. More recently considerable evidence has accumulated indicating that isolated soya bean protein has rachitogenic properties for

Estimates of requirement by the growing chick for vitamin D₃ with different levels of calcium and phosphorus

Source	Type of chick	Mineral levels (g/kg)		Criteria of adequacy	Estimated requirement, i.u./kg
		Ca	P		
Carver, Evans & McGinnis (1946)	(not stated)	5	5	Growth and bone ash	>200
		6	6		>200
		16 and 24	8		200
		30 and 40	10		200
Waldroup, Ammerman & Harms (1963)	Broilers to 4 weeks	4·8, 6·7, 8·6	4·8	Growth	400
				Bone ash	>400
		5·9, 8·3, 10·6	5·9	Growth	400
				Bone ash	>400
		7·0, 9·8, 12·6	7·0	Growth	400*
				Bone ash	>400
	Broilers to 4 weeks in batteries	5	5	Growth and bone ash	1600
		5	7		1600
		10	5		8000
		10	7		200*
Waldroup, Stearns, Ammerman & Harms (1965)	Broilers 0–8 weeks on litter	6	6·5	Growth and bone ash	800
		8	6·5		200*
		10	6·5		400*
Biely & March (1967)	New Hampshires to 8 weeks	7·5	6·5	Growth	600
		10	6·5	Growth and bone ash	400*

* Values used to estimate the requirements given in Table 4.5.

105

poultry. For turkey poults, Carlson, Saxena, Jensen and McGinnis (1964) found 880 i.u. vitamin D_3/kg adequate in a diet containing properly heated soya bean meal, but substitution by 30% isolated soya protein increased the vitamin D requirement eightfold. Rachitogenic activity was present also in whole raw soya bean meal, and a tenfold increase in the vitamin D supplement was needed to overcome it. Autoclaving destroyed the rachitogenic effect in both the isolated protein and in the uncooked meal. In contrast, heated soya bean meal was shown to be antirachitic for turkey poults (Carlson, McGinnis and Jensen, 1964). Chicks respond similarly, both to the rachitogenic action of isolated soya bean protein and to the antirachitic factor in heated soya meal (Jensen and Mraz, 1966). It has been suggested that the use of isolated soya protein or of inadequately heated soya bean meal may be responsible for unexplained outbreaks of rickets in turkey flocks.

Recent studies indicate an interrelationship between ascorbic acid and vitamin D in skeletal development in chicks. Thornton and Brownrigg (1961) observed that the progeny of hens given supplements of 44 or 88 mg ascorbic acid/kg diet had wider tibia epiphyseal plates than did progeny from unsupplemented hens. The difference was apparent whether or not the chicks received vitamin D in their diets; tibia ash and body weights were not influenced by the presence of vitamin C in the parental diet. However, in further studies Ramp and Thornton (1966) showed that injected ascorbic acid decreased the percentage of ash in tibias of rachitic chicks and Thornton (1968) showed that skeletal changes induced by a deficiency of vitamin D were all enhanced by inclusion of 220 mg/kg ascorbic acid in the diet. Neither of the last two studies was concerned with the effect of vitamin C on control chicks receiving adequate vitamin D. Although most avian species are capable of synthesizing ascorbic acid in quantities sufficient to cover their normal needs, dietary supplements of vitamin C have been claimed to confer benefit under some conditions of stress. In such circumstances the possible need for extra vitamin D deserves consideration.

VITAMIN E

FORMS OF VITAMIN E

The term "vitamin E" is applied to a group of compounds, the tocopherols, which have common biological properties. At least seven tocopherols occur naturally, but the only one to have important biological activity for poultry is alpha tocopherol. In nature, α-tocopherol occurs in the d-form whereas the substance produced by chemical synthesis is dl-α-tocopherol. The esters are more stable than the free tocopherols, hence dl-α-tocopheryl acetate is commonly used as a dietary supplement. The international unit is defined as the activity contained in 1 mg of a standard sample of dl-α-tocopheryl acetate. From the results of extensive tests with rats, Harris and Ludwig (1949) estimated that the potency of d-α-tocopheryl acetate is 1·36 i.u. vitamin E per mg. The calculated potencies of the free dl- and d-tocopherols are therefore 1·1 and 1·49 i.u./mg respectively.

The relative potency found in rat tests has more recently been confirmed in chicks. Pudelkiewicz, Matterson, Potter, Webster and Singsen (1960) found d-α-tocopherol to be 1·34 times as potent as the corresponding dl-form in an assay based on liver tocopherol levels in chicks. Marusich, Ackerman and Bauernfeind (1967) used a diet containing 5% safflower oil and assessed the chick's response in terms of plasma tocopherol levels and prevention of encephalomalacia. They confirmed the relative potency of the d- to dl- form as 1·36 to 1·0, whether the tocopherols were given in dry or oily preparations, continuously or in single doses, and by mouth or intramuscular injection. Dam

106

and Søndergaard (1964) found that the activities of d-, dl and l-α-tocopherols in reducing encephalomalacia in chicks given a diet with 30% lard were in the ratio of 1·7, 1·0 and 0·44 respectively. Their value of 1·7 is higher than the other two, but perhaps not significantly so.

EFFECTS OF DEPRIVATION

Vitamin E plays a multiple role in animal and avian nutrition. It functions as an antioxidant, both in the diet and in the tissues, and also plays a part, not yet fully understood, in several basic metabolic reactions. Thus the effects of a lack of vitamin E vary with different dietary and physiological conditions and some of its functions can be taken over, to a greater or lesser extent, by other substances not normally included among the vitamins (see, in particular, Selenium—*p* 82). An extensive review of the role of vitamin E in poultry nutrition has been compiled by Ames (1956). The chicken has proved a useful subject for studies of the biochemical role of vitamin E, and work in this field has been reviewed by Scott (1962a, b).

On diets containing high levels of unsaturated fats (for example, fish oils) the antioxidant properties of vitamin E predominate. Chicks, poults and ducklings reared on such diets develop encephalomalacia, a condition characterized by lesions in the cerebellum with consequent external signs of ataxia, muscular spasms and retraction of the neck. Fits of excited, unco-ordinated movement are followed by collapse, and death is frequently very sudden. The condition may be accompanied by a yellow discoloration of the body fat. The syndrome can be prevented by vitamin E and also by a variety of antioxidants such as ascorbic acid, diphenyl-p-phenylene diamine (DPPD), 6-ethoxy-1, 2-dihydro-2,2, 4-trimethylquinoline (ethoxyquin), butylated hydroxyanisole (BHA) and 2,6-di-tertiary-butyl-p-cresol (BHT). Much higher quantities of the anti-oxidants than of tocopherol are required and their mechanism of action is still controversial. It has been suggested that their chief function is to stabilise the available quantites of vitamin E in the diet or tissues. An alternative proposal is that antioxidants are directly involved in tissue metabolism; they may, for instance, increase the catabolism of unsaturated fatty acids and thereby reduce the need for vitamin E (Bunnell, Matterson, Singsen and Eaton, 1956).

Vitamin E deficiency can develop on diets without high levels of unsaturated fat and in this event antioxidants are ineffective in reversing the condition (Dam, Prange and Søndergaard, 1952). The most obvious sign is exudative diathesis, in which increased capillary permeability gives rise to haemorrhagic oedema of the subcutaneous tissues, manifested by bruise-like patches of discolouration on the breast and legs. Haemorrhages also occur in the intestinal wall. There is a loss of blood proteins in the exudate and a decreased level of synthesis of plasma albumin (Goldstein and Scott, 1956). An increased fragility of the red blood cells (Muytjens, 1956) and loss of blood in the exudate together might be expected to lead to a macrocytic anaemia, but since the anaemia observed by Scott, Hill, Norris, Dobson and Nelson (1955) was microcytic they suggest that vitamin E may play a role in erythropoiesis. The condition of exudative diathesis can be prevented or cured by inorganic selenium compounds or by vitamin E. Nesheim and Scott (1958) showed that sodium selenite completely prevented exudative diathesis in chicks given a diet low in vitamin E and selenium, but both vitamin E and selenium were necessary to maintain full growth potential. The curative effect of dried brewers' yeast has been attributed to its content of selenium (Nesheim and Scott, 1958).

A third condition commonly observed in young birds deprived of vitamin E is muscular dystrophy, in which degenerated muscle fibres are visible as white

107

striations in the breast and legs. Antioxidants are ineffective in preventing muscular dystrophy. Supplements of selenium reduce the incidence but do not entirely prevent it (Nesheim and Scott, 1958). Early studies by Dam, Prange and Søndergaard (1952) showed that muscular dystrophy in chicks could be prevented by dietary supplements of cystine. Later suggestions that methionine was equally effective (Machlin and Shalkop, 1956) have not been entirely confirmed (Scott and Calvert, 1962). According to Nesheim, Calvert and Scott (1960) addition of 10 g arginine/kg to a diet low in vitamin E and cystine exacerbated the occurrence of muscular dystrophy; in these circumstances methionine was protective. However, although arginine could counteract the protective effect of 2·5 g DL-methionine/kg it could not precipitate muscular dystrophy in chicks given a similar diet with 2 g cystine/kg in place of the methionine (Scott and Calvert, 1962). There are indications from more recent work that cysteine, or a derivative of it, may be the sulphur-containing amino acid directly concerned in prevention of muscular dystrophy (Hathcock, Scott and Thompson, 1968). It is possible that the heart distension observed in young chicks deprived of vitamin E (Bird, Culton and Kline, 1940) and the abnormal electrocardiograms reported in older birds (Sturkie, Singsen, Matterson, Kozeff and Jungherr, 1954) may be associated with degenerative changes in heart muscle. Erosion of the smooth muscle of the wall of the gizzard as a result of vitamin E deficiency was first reported in young turkeys (Jungherr and Pappenheimer, 1937-38) and has also been seen in chicks (Jungherr, 1949; Zacharias, Goldhaber and Kinsey, 1950).

Vitamin E appears to be involved in the prevention of hock disorders in turkeys, although other nutritional factors are concerned as well. Scott (1953) described enlarged hocks and bowed legs in poults given a diet containing 20 to 40 g cod liver oil/kg; the condition was curable with supplements of vitamin E and nicotinic acid. A hock disorder in older turkeys responded to the same treatment. Signs of enlarged hocks, bowed legs and perosis were prevented by a combination of vitamin E and inorganic phosphorus (Slinger, Pepper and Motzok, 1954).

It has long been known that vitamin E is essential for reproduction in rats. In breeding birds also a lack of vitamin E is detrimental to reproductive performance in the male and female. Reduced hatchability has been observed in the fowl and turkey hen deprived of vitamin E. In cocks on a diet with high linoleic acid, deficiency of vitamin E resulted in lowered fertilizing capacity and sperm concentration; both conditions were reversed by supplying vitamin E or ethoxyquin (Arscott, Parker and Dickinson, 1965; Arscott and Parker, 1967; Kuhns and Arscott, 1969). In the Japanese quail Price (1968) noted reduced fertility in the male but not in the female deprived of vitamin E.

ASSESSMENT OF REQUIREMENT

It is clear from the foregoing information that no statement of requirement would be valid in all circumstances. The extent to which vitamin E is needed in a diet will depend on the nature of the other constituents. In particular the oxidising or antioxidant properties of the diet, its content of selenium and its amino acid balance are likely to exert an important influence.

A number of workers have tried to estimate the vitamin E requirements of different classes of poultry under a variety of dietary conditions and their results are summarised in Table 4.4. From these results tentative values have been derived and inserted in Tables 4.5 and 4.6, but it must be emphasized that they have been given only as a guide. They may be considerably in excess of the true requirement when all dietary "stress factors" are absent, or when the diet

Table 4.4

Estimates of vitamin E requirement for poultry given different types of diet

Source	Dietary 'stress' factor	Signs of deficiency	Estimated vitamin E requirement i.u./kg	Alternative effective substances
Chicks				
Singsen, Bunnell, Matterson, Kozeff & Jungherr (1955)	None	None	<7	
	Fish liver oil (20 g/kg)	Encephalomalacia	24	125 mg DPPD/kg
Scott, Norris, Heuser & Nelson (1955)	Torula yeast and lard	Encephalomalacia	15 to 30	
Scott, Hill, Norris, Dobson & Nelson (1955)	Torula yeast and lard	Exudative diathesis	15	100 g dried brewers yeast /kg
	Low protein	Microcytic anaemia	15	100 g dried brewers yeast/kg
Nesheim & Scott (1958)	Isolated soya protein	Exudative diathesis	44	100 g dried brwers yeast/kg; 0·1 mg Na$_2$SeO$_3$/kg; 1 mg seleno-cystathione/kg
	Torula yeast	Exudative diathesis	>110	0·14 mg Na$_2$SeO$_3$/kg
Scott (1962b)	Deficient in methionine, cystine, Se and vitamin E, but added antioxidants	Exudative diathesis / Muscular dystrophy	5 / 20	0·1 mg Na$_2$SeO$_3$/kg / 0·1 mg Na$_2$SeO$_3$ + 10 i.u. vitamin E/kg; or 1·0 mg Na$_2$SeO$_3$ + 5 i.u. vitamin E/kg
Scott & Calvert (1962)	Isolated soya protein; diet low in methionine and cystine	Muscular dystrophy	11	15 g cystine/kg

continued on next page)

109

Table 4.4 (*continued*)

Source	Dietary "stress" factor	Signs of deficiency	Estimated vitamin E requirement i.u./kg	Alternative effective substances
Turkey poults Scott (1953)	Cod liver oil (20 to 40 g/kg)	Enlarged hock	15 (plus 44 mg nicotinic acid/kg)	10 g dried brewers yeast + 5·5 i.u. vitamin E/kg; or 5·5 mg BHA + 5·5 i.u. vitmain E/kg
Slinger, Pepper & Motzok (1954)	Low level of inorganic P	Englarged hock, perosis	11 (plus 5 g inorganic P/kg)	
Turkey hens Jensen, Carver & McGinnis (1955)	Fish liver oil (20 g/kg)	Reduced hatchability	>44	250 mg DPPD/kg
Atkinson, Ferguson, Quisenberry & Couch (1955)	All vegetable protein	Reduced hatchability	60	

110

contains some or all of the substances with vitamin E-like activity. Conversely, in view of one or two very high estimates among those shown in Table 4.4, there are apparently circumstances in which the tentative estimate would be too low.

VITAMIN K

FORMS OF VITAMIN K

It is not feasible to discuss the requirements for vitamin K without considering the different forms in which it occurs, and their relative biological potencies. The naturally occurring forms are vitamin K_1 (phylloquinone; 2-methyl-3-phytyl-1, 4-naphthoquinone) from plant sources, particularly green leaves, and vitamin K_2 (menaquinone-7; 2-methyl-3-difarnesyl-1, 4-naphthoquinone) which is synthesized by micro-organisms. Vitamin K_3 (menaphthone; 2-methyl-1, 4-napthoquinone) is a chemically synthesized fat-soluble compound, and two of its water-soluble derivatives are menaphthone sodium bisulphite (MSB) and menaphthone sodium diphosphate. A more stable complex of MSB, with extra sodium bisulphite (MSBC) is also available. These are the five compounds of most importance in avian nutrition although other naphthoquinones have, vitamin K activity (Matschiner and Doisy, 1966; see also review by Griminger, 1966a). A dimethyl pyrimidinol bisulphite derivative of menaphthone has recently been developed and is reported to be more active than MSB (Griminger, 1965a; Dua and Day, 1966).

In terms of relative molecular weights 1 mg vitamin K_1 is equivalent to 0·73 mg MSB or 0·38 mg menaphthone, and their relative biological activities are best considered on this molar basis. In an extensive study Nelson and Norris (1960) found that for chicks the requirement, in mg/kg diet, of vitamin K_1, MSB and menaphthone respectively was 0·528, 0·357 and 0·479; expressed in moles/kg diet the respective requirements were 1·17, 1·08 and 2·79, Thus vitamin K_1 and MSB were, on a molar basis, equally effective and both were about 2·5 times as active as menaphthone. The comparisons were made with a diet containing no stress factors but there is evidence, to be discussed later, that the relative potencies are different when a diet contains certain vitamin K antagonists. Griminger (1966a) has summarized the findings of twelve investigations and concludes that vitamin K_1 is the most active and that menaphthone has a much lower potency than either of the other two. There are suggestions that the transfer of vitamin K_1 from parent to offspring is more efficient than that of menaphthone (Brubacher, Friesecke, Streiff and Wiss, 1959) or MSB (Griminger, 1964).

EFFECTS OF DEPRIVATION

According to Almquist (1954) the only primary effect in animals of a lack of vitamin K is upon the prothrombin level of the blood, which is decreased. Thus the clotting time of the blood is prolonged and severe haemorrhage results from comparatively minor injury. Chicks and poults deprived of vitamin K show haemorrhages on the breast, legs and wings, as well as internally in the abdominal cavity and on the surface of the intestines. Chicks become anaemic, not only through loss of blood but also because hypoplasia of the bone marrow develops (Scott, 1966). Early investigators considered gizzard erosion to be one of the signs of vitamin K deficiency but later work has shown that it is not specific and may arise from other nutritional defects. Nevertheless, in the experiments of Frost, Perdue and Spruth (1956) incidence of gizzard erosion was related to the severity of vitamin K deficiency. These authors observed that growth was not affected except in very severe deficiency.

111

There have been few studies in adult birds. Griminger (1964) reported high embryonic mortality in eggs from SCWL hens deprived of vitamin K; most of the deaths occurred after the eighteenth day of incubation and haemorrhagic areas were seen on a number of the dead embryos. A number of recent investigators have reported a relationship between the incidence of blood spots in eggs and the dietary vitamin K status of the hen. It has been postulated that the presence of sufficient vitamin K causes blood in the eggs to clot, and thus become visible, instead of diffusing through the albumen (Fry, Waldroup, Damron, Harms and Wilson, 1968). These workers observed a reduced incidence of blood spots when hens were given a diet very low in vitamin K, but no adverse effects on egg production, hatchability or viability of the chicks.

Although outbreaks of haemorrhagic disease are encountered in practice, veterinary investigations indicate that they are rarely due to simple deficiency of vitamin K and may arise from totally different causes (Gray, Snoeyenbos and Reynolds, 1954; Cover, Mellen and Gill, 1955).

ASSESSMENT OF REQUIREMENTS

The requirement of the chick for vitamin K has been most extensively studied by Nelson and Norris (1960, 1961a) and their figure of about 0·5 mg vitamin K_1/kg diet seems the best estimate. In their first investigation 0·528 mg vitamin K/kg was adequate for chicks up to four weeks of age; in the later one 0·515 mg/kg was sufficient to maintain normal prothrombin times in chicks to 12 weeks. Assuming that, on a molar basis, MSB is equally effective and menaphthone only 40% effective, the corresponding requirements/kg diet would be 0·35 mg MSB and 0·475 mg menaphthone. For turkey poults Griminger (1957) found that 1·1 mg MSB (or 1·5 mg vitamin K_1)/kg diet was needed to support normal prothrombin times to four weeks of age. Pheasants and quail required only 0·062 mg MSB or a stabilized preparation of vitamin K_1/kg diet to prevent signs of deficiency (Scott, Holm and Reynolds, 1961).

Evidence on the vitamin K requirement of laying and breeding hens is sparse and contradictory. From the results of an investigation with small groups of SCWL hens Griminger (1964) suspected that 1 mg vitamin K_1 or MSBC/kg diet might not be adequate to support optimal hatchability. Conversely, Fry, Waldroup, Damron, Harms and Wilson (1968) estimated that only 0·2 to 0·4 mg MSBC/kg diet was needed. However, since Griminger used a diet of purified ingredients less likely than the corn-soya diet of Fry *et al.* to contribute vitamin K, his value of at least 1 mg/kg has been chosen as the most probable estimate of requirement.

FACTORS AFFECTING REQUIREMENT FOR VITAMIN K

Microbial synthesis

Vitamin K_2 is synthesized by micro-organisms of the alimentary tract; hence birds with access to their own excreta can obtain all or part of their requirement through coprophagy. It is doubtful whether the microbially synthesized vitamin K is available to the bird by direct absorption from the gut. An early report (Almquist and Stokstad, 1936) described the presence of vitamin K in freshly voided faeces from chicks given a diet free from vitamin K, although this has not been confirmed by later workers. Neither Scott (1955) nor Griminger (1957) could detect vitamin K in fresh chicken or poult faeces when care was taken to prevent fermentation after voiding. Vitamin K appeared in poult faeces that had been left to stand without a bacteriostat for 48 hours (Griminger, 1957), hence it seems likely that it can be synthesized aerobically after the faeces have been passed. In contrast to what happens in the rat, caecal synthesis of vitamin

K does not appear to be nutritionally important to the chicken, since Nelson and Norris (1961a) failed to observe spontaneous recovery from vitamin K deficiency in chicks maintained for sixteen weeks with no dietary source of the vitamin. Nevertheless, the prothrombin times of caecectomized chicks became progressively shorter than those of intact controls, and the authors postulated that the small intestine had taken over some of the functions of the caecum with consequently greater chance of absorption of any vitamin K_2 that had been synthesized. These results justify the supposition that, although vitamin K_2 is formed by microbial action in the alimentary tract of birds, the sites of its formation are too distal to permit absorption of significant quantities without coprophagy.

Antagonists to vitamin K

It is generally agreed that drugs of the sulphonamide series can induce signs of vitamin K deficiency in mammals and birds. In view of the use of drugs such as sulphamethazine and sulphaquinoxaline in the treatment of coccidiosis in poultry it is important to know the extent of their antivitamin K activity. Earlier literature has been reviewed by Nelson and Norris (1959), who confirmed that inclusion of 1 g sulphaquinoxaline/kg of diet exacerbated the signs of deficiency in chicks given a diet low in vitamin K; addition of 2·5 mg MSB/kg of diet restored clotting time to normal. Frost, Perdue and Spruth (1956) also reported that 1 g sulphaquinoxaline/kg of diet increased the chick's requirement for vitamin K and that MSB was six to ten times as effective as menaphthone in reversing the hypoprothrombinaemia. They suggested that the water-soluble MSB might be more readily absorbed, although they were unable to improve the utilization of either menaphthone or MSB by including up to 40 g/kg of extra fat in the diet. Nelson and Norris (1961b) made a study of the effects of sulphaquinoxaline on the quantitative requirements of the chick for different forms of vitamin K and found that on a molar basis, the relative efficacy of vitamin K_1, MSB and menaphthone in overcoming the toxicity of 1 g sulphaquinoxaline/kg was in the ratio of 100:70:40. The requirement for vitamin K_1 was increased four to seven times. Similarly in the experiments of Griminger and Donis (1960) the chick's need for vitamin K was increased at least fourfold by inclusion of 2 g sulphaquinoxaline/kg of diet. The mechanism of the antivitamin K action of the sulphonamides is not known. As Nelson and Norris (1959) point out, it is unlikely to be directly due to interference with bacterial synthesis as the bird appears to derive little contribution to its requirement of the vitamin by this means. They suggest that the drugs may have some inhibitory effect on the metabolism of vitamin K in the tissues.

Other substances that have been shown to increase vitamin K requirement in the chick are vitamin A (in massive doses), the tetracycline antibiotics and arsanilic acid, but their effect is relatively slight and readily overcome by moderate increases in vitamin K intake. Of more serious consequence are the coumarin-type anti-coagulants (for example, warfarin, 3-(α-acetonylbenzyl)-4-hydroxycoumarin) that are known to have a profoundly inhibitory action in the mechanism of blood clotting. Griminger (1965b) compared the antivitamin K activity of vitamin A (220 000 i.u./kg diet), tetracycline (500 mg/kg diet) sulphadimethoxine (2 g/kg diet) and warfarin (0·5 to 500 mg/kg diet), and the counteractivity of MSBC and vitamin K_1. Vitamin A and tetracycline prolonged prothrombin times only at low levels of vitamin K intake, and no adverse effect was apparent with diets containing 0·6 mg or more vitamin K_1/kg. Sulphadimethoxine increased the requirement by a factor of two or three, and MSBC was as effective as vitamin K_1 in overcoming the hypoprothrombinaemia. Warfarin, however, vastly increased the need for vitamin K and 400 to 500 mg vitamin K_1/kg diet were required to overcome the anticoagulant action of 100 mg warfarin/kg; MSBC was virtually ineffective.

Disease

Since internal haemorrhage is one of the major effects of coccidial infestation it is perhaps not surprising that addition of dicoumarol to the diet significantly increases the mortality of chicks suffering from caecal coccidiosis (Harms and Tugwell, 1956) or that supplementation of a vitamin K-low diet with MSBC exerts a protective effect (Tugwell, Stephens and Harms, 1957; Otto, Jeske, Frost and Perdue, 1957). In a comparison of the ability of different forms of vitamin K to protect chicks against the effects of caecal coccidiosis Harms, Waldroup and Cox (1960) reduced mortality in experimentally infected chicks from 98 to 46% with additions of 0·5 mg vitamin K_1/kg of diet low in vitamin K. Weight for weight, vitamin K_1 was about four times as effective as MSBC, which in turn was six to seven times as effective as menaphthone (on a molar

Table 4.5
Fat-soluble vitamin requirements of fowls

	Preferred estimate of requirement	Range of selected values	No. of values	Sources
Vitamin A, i.u./kg				
Chicks	1320	830 to 1730	6	4, 8, 12, 16
Layers and breeders	2700	2640 to 2750	2	8, 13
Vitamin D_3, i.u./kg				
Chicks	400	200 to 400	5	2, 14, 15
Layers and breeders	600	500 to 780	4	1, 3, 5, 9
Vitamin E, i.u./kg				
Chicks	15*	—		
Layers and breeders	?			
Vitamin K,† mg/kg				
Chicks	0·5	0·5	2	10, 11
Layers and breeders	1·0*	0·4 to 1·0	2	6, 7

* Tentative estimates only (see text).
† As vitamin K_1. 1 mg vitamin K_1 is equivalent to 0·73 mg menaphthone sodium bisulphite.

Key to sources

1. Bethke *et al.* (1937)
2. Biely & March (1967)
3. Correll & Wise (1938)
4. Donovan (1965a)
5. Evans *et al.* (1944)
6. Fry *et al.* (1968)
7. Griminger (1964)
8. Hill *et al.* (1961)
9. Murphy *et al.* (1936)
10. Nelson & Norris (1960)
11. Nelson & Norris (1961a)
12. Olsen *et al.* (1964)
13. Reid *et al.* (1965)
14. Waldroup *et al.* (1963)
15. Waldroup *et al.* (1965)
16. Wilson & Teekell (1966)

basis these ratios would be twice and five times respectively). In a later study they reported that coccidiosis did not appear to increase the chick's requirement for vitamin K, and confirmed the relatively greater efficacy of vitamin K_1 compared with that of MSBC (Harms, Waldroup and Cox, 1962).

Vitamin K has been shown to increase the chick's resistance to other diseases. Hill and Garren (1957b) noted that supplements of 55 to 110 mg MSB or menaphthone/kg added to a diet that contained high levels of other essential vitamins decreased mortality of chicks experimentally infected with *Salmonella gallinarum*. The protective action was apparently not connected with the antihaemorrhagic properties of vitamin K since prothrombin times were not affected by the supplement. Increased prothrombin times were observed by Squibb (1964) in chicks during an outbreak of Newcastle disease. It occurred only in birds on a diet low in vitamin K and could be prevented by inclusion of

Table 4.6
Fat-soluble vitamin requirements of turkeys, ducks, geese and pheasants

	Preferred estimate of requirement	Range of selected values	No. of values	Sources
Vitamin A, i.u./kg				
Turkey poult	1760	—	1	10
Breeding turkey	2700	—	2	5, 10
Vitamin D_3, i.u./kg				
Turkey poult	900	550 to 1100	2	6, 11
Breeding turkey	2000	—	1	9
Duckling	300	280 to 350	3	1, 2, 4
Gosling	300	—	1	2
Pheasant chick	1100	—	1	7
Vitamin E, i.u./kg				
Turkey poult	15*			
Breeding turkey	60*			
Vitamin K,† mg/kg				
Turkey poult	1·5	—	1	3
Breeding turkey	?			
Pheasant chick	0·06	—	1	8

* Tentative estimates only (see text).
† As vitamin K_1. 1 mg vitamin K_1 is equivalent to 0·73 mg menaphthone sodium bisulphite.

Key to sources

1. Black & Coates (1948)
2. Fritz *et al.* (1941)
3. Griminger (1957)
4. Motzok & Branion (1948)
5. Jensen (1965)
6. Neagle *et al.* (1968)

7. Scott *et al.* (1958)
8. Scott *et al.* (1961)
9. Stadelman *et al.* (1950)
10. Stoewsand & Scott (1961a)
11. Sullivan & Kingan (1963)

0·125 mg MSB/kg diet, by transfer to a commercial diet or by a single injection of 0·24 mg MSB/chick. Nelson and Norris (1959) noted that blood clotting times of chicks with a low vitamin K intake were prolonged during the days following vaccination against infectious bronchitis; clotting times were normal in the blood of similar chicks receiving 0·5 mg or more MSB/kg diet. All these findings suggest that the stress of exposure to disease may produce at least a temporary increase in the chick's need for vitamin K.

THIAMIN

Thiamin (vitamin B_1) is available commercially as the hydrochloride and it is usually in this form that it is added to experimental diets.

EFFECTS OF DEPRIVATION

In young birds severe deprivation of thiamin results in poor growth and polyneuritis, a condition characterised by leg weakness and ataxia; a backward retraction of the head usually develops in chicks but not in poults. There is a high mortality, possibly due to heart failure, and death is frequently preceded by convulsions. Thiamin is required for normal embryo development, hence poor hatchability is a feature of eggs from hens with an inadequate intake. Transketolase activity in the red blood cells is reduced in thiamin deficiency and has been proposed by Padhi and Combs (1965) as an index of thiamin status.

ASSESSMENT OF REQUIREMENT

The previous value for the chick of 1·0 mg/kg diet has been retained. This is based largely on the work of Thornton and Shutze (1960), who found 0·9 mg/kg adequate for all breeds and of Abbott, Bird and Cravens (1954) whose experiments indicated that between 1·0 and 1·2 mg/kg supported optimal growth for the first few weeks of life.

From a study in SCWL pullets, Padhi and Combs (1965) found 1·25 mg thiamin/kg diet necessary to prevent signs of polyneuritis and to maintain egg production and maximal levels of transketolase activity in the red blood cells. Polin, Wynosky and Porter (1962) assessed the minimal free thiamin level in the yolk necessary for normal hatchability to be 0·63 mg/kg. Polin, Ott, Wynosky and Porter (1963) calculated that a level of 0·68 mg/kg diet was necessary to attain this amount in the yolk. However, since this value was found by extrapolation from results of experiments with higher levels of thiamin, and the authors point out that 0·68 mg/kg would only be adequate so long as feed intake were normal, it seems wiser to recommend the higher level of Padhi and Combs (1965).

Two studies have been made of the thiamin requirements of turkey poults. Robenalt (1960) found 1 mg/kg diet adequate for poults to 12 days of age but 2 mg/kg was needed for optimal growth beyond that stage. A more recent investigation by Sullivan, Heil and Armintrout (1967) indicates that between 1·6 and 2·0 mg/kg is necessary, maximal growth and survival time at 4 weeks of age being attained with 2·0 mg/kg. This value has been used in the table of requirements.

Breed

Breed differences with respect to susceptibility to thiamin deficiency have been reported by a number of workers. Lamoreux and Hutt (1939) concluded that light breeds had a lower requirement than heavy breeds since WL chicks survived longer than RIR chicks on a diet deficient in thiamin. This view was supported by reports of higher deposits of thiamin in the egg of WL hens compared with those of heavier breeds, indicating more efficient utilization and therefore a smaller dietary requirement by the WL hens (Scrimshaw, Hutt and Scrimshaw, 1945; Howes and Hutt, 1956; Mayfield, Roehm and Beeckler, 1955). The opposite conclusion has been reached by Thornton (1960a) from the results of experiments in which graded dietary levels of thiamin were given to Leghorn crossbred and NH × Delaware chicks. Although the mean survival time was very slightly longer in the Leghorn chicks, they nevertheless required a higher dietary supplement than did the heavier breed for maintenance of optimal growth and prevention of signs of polyneuritis and mortality. It is clear that the question of genetic variation in thiamin requirement needs further study. However, the value of 0·9 mg/kg was considered by Thornton and Shutze (1960) to cover the requirement of Leghorn and broiler-type chicks.

Other constituents of the diet

Since thiamin plays a specific role in the metabolism of carbohydrate it is to be expected than an increase in the carbohydrate content of the diet would increase the need for thiamin. Such a relationship has been shown to exist in mammals and furthermore, replacement of carbohydrate by fat has a sparing effect on thiamin requirement. In broiler chicks on a thiamin deficient diet Thornton and Shutze (1960) demonstrated similar effects. Peacock and Combs (1969) also noted a reduced requirement for thiamin when the major energy source was fat instead of carbohydrate. Thus for diets in which a considerable portion of the energy content is supplied as fat the values given in the table of requirements may be higher than necessary.

Non-nutrient additives

Certain chemical compounds have been shown to antagonise the action of thiamin in the animal body. Of particular interest in poultry feeding is the coccidiostat, amprolium (1-(4-amino-2-n-propyl-5-pyrimidinyl-methyl)-2-picolinium chloride hydrochloride). Ott, Dickinson and van Iderstine (1965) have estimated that the effects of thiamin in sustaining growth and preventing the development of polyneuritis are counteracted by about 500 times its weight of the drug. Thus at the recommended level for use as a coccidiostat (125 mg/kg of diet) amprolium is unlikely seriously to increase the bird's requirement for the vitamin.

RIBOFLAVIN

EFFECTS OF DEPRIVATION

Riboflavin is essential for the maintenance of growth in young birds. On an inadequate intake turkey poults develop dermatitis and chicks exhibit a deformity characterised by an inward curling of the toes ("curled toe paralysis"); more severe deficiency results in irreversible paralysis due to degeneration of the sciatic and brachial nerves. Eggs from hens deprived of riboflavin fail to hatch. The peak embryonic mortality occurs during the second week of incubation, the embryos are dwarfed and frequently show "clubbing" of the down.

The requirements for riboflavin of most classes of poultry are well established and there has been little recent work to challenge the levels hitherto recommended. Experiments in Japan, however, indicate possible breed differences in requirement. Yoshida, Hoshii and Morimoto (1966) found that, under their conditions, broiler-type chicks (White Cornish × New Hampshire) needed 7·2 mg riboflavin/kg to maintain optimal growth and prevent curled toe paralysis whereas WL chicks performed normally on 5·5 mg/kg. They attributed the increased requirement of the broiler cross to the influence of the White Cornish sires, since the NH dams had been satisfactorily reared on a lower intake of riboflavin. There is some evidence of a more efficient use of riboflavin by WL compared with NH hens since, on the same diet, the WL birds deposited significantly greater amounts in the egg (Mayfield, Roehm and Beeckler, 1955). Strain differences within the WL breed in susceptibility to riboflavin deficiency have been demonstrated by Lamoreux and Hutt (1948) and Lerner and Bird (1948). A special case of inherited riboflavin deficiency in SCWL embryos was attributed by Maw (1954) to a recessive gene which prevented the transfer to the egg of sufficient riboflavin for normal embryo development.

NICOTINIC ACID

Nicotinic acid and its corresponding amide are both produced commercially by chemical synthesis. The two compounds have similar biological potency for poultry.

EFFECTS OF DEPRIVATION

In young birds deprived of nicotinic acid growth is retarded and feathering poor. Perosis is frequently observed and, in poults, there may be an enlargement of the hocks. In severe deficiency the inside of the mouth becomes red and inflamed, although the tongue tip is blanched; "parrot beak", in which the beak appears shortened and arched, may develop. In older birds nicotinic acid is essential for the maintenance of normal egg production and hatchability.

ASSESSMENT OF REQUIREMENT

The previous recommendations for the nicotinic acid requirements of young birds are unaltered, and it is now possible to provide a value for the amount needed by laying and breeding hens. The results of experiments by Ringrose, Manoukas, Hinkson and Teeri (1964, 1965), with three different breeds, suggest that 0·8 mg/hen day is necessary for egg production and 1·0 mg/hen day for optimal hatchability; by conversion to an estimated feed intake of 100 g/hen day the requirements become 8 and 10 mg/kg diet respectively. There was no evidence for a difference in requirement between breeds. Although Adams and Carrick (1967) concluded that 0·73 mg nicotinic acid/hen day (7·3 mg/kg diet) was more than adequate to maintain egg production and hatchability in WL pullets, the higher estimate of the previous workers has been chosen for safety.

FACTORS AFFECTING REQUIREMENT

Tryptophan

Since L-tryptophan is the precursor from which nicotinic acid is synthesized in animal tissues, the dietary requirement for nicotinic acid is to some extent dependent on the supply of available tryptophan. It is now generally agreed that, although excess nicotinic acid cannot compensate for a lack of tryptophan, supplements of tryptophan over and above the basic requirement of approximately 1·7 g/kg can reduce the bird's requirement for nicotinic acid. The values given in the tables are based on experiments with diets containing about 1·5 g tryptophan/kg of diet. According to Patterson, Hunt, Vohra, Blaylock and McGinnis (1956) chicks grew adequately and did not develop perosis on a diet containing 2·4 g tryptophan and 18 to 20 mg nicotinic acid/kg diet. However, with only 1·4 g tryptophan/kg, a level of between 29 and 33 mg nicotinic acid/kg was needed. This indicates that about 70 to 100 mg tryptophan spared 1 mg of the vitamin. In a study with WL hens, using hatchability as the criterion of nicotinic acid status, it was estimated that 187 mg tryptophan were equivalent to 1 mg nicotinic acid (Manoukas, Ringrose and Teeri, 1968). Other results with young chicks range from failure to spare nicotinic acid with tryptophan (West, Carrick, Hauge and Mertz, 1952) to complete replacement of the vitamin with 2 g tryptophan/kg (Fisher, Scott and Johnson, 1954). For all practical purposes it would seem wise to accept the opinion of Childs, Carrick and Hauge (1952) that a diet high in tryptophan might be of value in correcting a marginal deficiency of nicotinic acid, but cannot be relied upon to compensate for more severe deficiency.

Availability from cereals

Most of the nicotinic acid in cereals occurs in a "bound" form which is not fully available to higher animals unless treated with alkali. Acute signs of nicotinic acid deficiency were observed in ducklings on a diet containing 71 % yellow maize (Hegsted, 1946), and Heuser and Scott (1953) observed that ducklings utilized nicotinic acid from wheat middlings very poorly. Chick assays of an extract of wheat bran detected only about half the nicotinic acid present before, and the full quantity after, treatment with alkali (Krehl, Elvehjem and Strong, 1944).

In recent studies Manoukas *et al.* (1968) estimated the availability to hens of nicotinic acid in maize, wheat middlings and soya bean meal. Nicotinic acid was determined microbiologically in the feeds and also assayed biologically in terms of the effect on hatchability of eggs. Comparison of the results by the two methods showed that the nicotinic acid in heated soya bean meal was fully available to the hen but that only 30 and 36 % was utilized from maize meal and wheat bran respectively. In view of these results it is recommended that in calculating the nicotinic acid content of practical poultry diets little account be taken of the amount provided by the cereal components.

PANTOTHENIC ACID

Pantothenic acid occurs naturally in the d-form. The free acid is unstable and calcium pantothenate is the product used in commerce. This can be prepared synthetically as calcium d- or dl- pantothenate, the latter having about half the biological value of the former.

EFFECTS OF DEPRIVATION

In young birds deprived of pantothenic acid there is a depression of growth rate. Lesions at the corners of the mouth and a sticky exudate from the eyes, causing the eyelids to remain closed, are characteristic signs of deficiency. In the later stages there may be a scaly dermatitis of the feet. In laying birds egg production is depressed and hatchability is very seriously reduced. Beer, Scott and Nesheim (1963) have described abnormalities in the embryos of dams given

119

diets low in pantothenic acid. At first the peak mortality occurred at 22 days, with many chicks pipping the shell but failing to hatch; as the deficiency progressed the peak of mortality became earlier and the dead-in-shell embryos showed patches of subcutaneous haemorrhage or blebs of fluid under the skin. The authors point out, however, that such severe abnormalities are unlikely to be encountered in practice.

ASSESSMENT OF REQUIREMENTS

There is little to add to the previous assessments of requirements apart from the work of Beer *et al.* (1963), whose conclusions regarding the requirements of laying and breeding pullets are in agreement with earlier estimates. It is clear that very much higher levels are necessary for good hatchability than for maintenance of egg production, and that the reserves carried over in the egg are of importance to the young growing chick. The earlier findings of Gillis, Heuser and Norris (1948) that 8 mg pantothenic acid/kg were necessary in the diet of breeding hens for good growth and viability of progeny was confirmed by Beer *et al.* (1963) when they used a chick diet containing only 1·1 mg pantothenic acid/kg. However, a lower carryover can be tolerated by chicks receiving the recommended level of 10 mg/kg diet.

FACTORS AFFECTING REQUIREMENT

There is a relationship between dietary vitamin B_{12} and pantothenic acid. Several investigators have shown that vitamin B_{12} deficiency in chick diets increases the need for pantothenic acid, and in breeding hens Balloun and Phillips (1957) estimated that the requirement for pantothenic acid was increased from 6 or 7 mg/kg on a diet adequate in vitamin B_{12} to 9 or 10 mg/kg on a diet deficient in vitamin B_{12}.

Beer *et al.* (1963) comment that although theoretically most practical poultry diets should contain enough naturally occurring pantothenic acid, nevertheless cases of pantothenic acid deficiency do occur in the field. These could be due to over-heating of the diet during processing, to bad storage conditions or possible unknown antimetabolites of the vitamin in the other ingredients.

PYRIDOXINE

FORMS OF PYRIDOXINE

Pyridoxine (vitamin B_6) occurs in nature as pyridoxol, pyridoxamine, pyridoxal and their corresponding phosphates. All are equally effective for the chick when given directly by mouth or injection. However, pyridoxamine and pyridoxal are not completely stable when distributed in a diet (Davis, Gregory and Henry, 1959), which may explain previous reports of their lower efficacy compared with pyridoxol as sources of vitamin B_6 for the chick.

EFFECT OF DEPRIVATION

The effects of a lack of vitamin B_6 in chicks and poults are obvious within a week of hatching. The birds grow very poorly and become extremely excitable; trembling fits and convulsions precede death, and the mortality rate is high. Some workers have reported gizzard erosion and patches of haemorrhage, particularly round the follicles of the wing feathers (Daghir and Balloun, 1963). In severe deficiency there are profound biochemical changes, including a reduction in plasma proteins and in several circulating enzymes, particularly glutamic-oxalacetic transaminase. However, at least two groups of investigators have found these parameters to be less sensitive than growth as indicators of vitamin B$_6$ adequacy (Daghir and Balloun, 1963; Kirchgessner and Maier, 1968a). Gehle and Balloun (1965) reported that chicks deprived of vitamin B$_6$ became anaemic due to a failure in the normal mechanisms of haemoglobin synthesis. They also concluded, as a result of pair-feeding trails, that the deficiency depressed appetite and that many deaths were a direct result of starvation. In laying and breeding birds a lack of vitamin B$_6$ diminishes egg production and hatchability.

ASSESSMENT OF REQUIREMENT

In recent years several further attempts to determine the vitamin B$_6$ requirement of the chick have been made. Two investigations in Germany, in which semi-purified diets were used, assess the requirement of crossbred broiler chicks at 5 or 6 mg/kg diet (Kirchgessner and Friesecke, 1963; Kirchgessner and Maier, 1968b). However, the same workers recommended only 3 mg/kg for chicks given a practical type diet (Maier and Kirchgessner, 1967). Daghir and Balloun (1963) found 2·6 mg/kg in a semi-purified diet adequate for three different breeds. As these new estimates fall on either side of the previous recommendation, the value of 3·5 mg/kg has been retained but the upper range limit is increased to 5·5 mg/kg. For turkey poults a figure of 4·0 mg/kg has been preferred to the previous estimate of 3·0 mg/kg (Kratzer, Bird, Asmundson and Lepkovsky, 1947). This has been done on the grounds that the recent work (Sullivan, Heil and Armintrout, 1967) is more likely to be relevant to modern conditions. Furthermore, it was determined in poults given a semi-purified, diet, whereas the diet used by the earlier workers could have contributed a small amount of vitamin B$_6$ that was not taken into account in the assessment of requirement.

FACTORS AFFECTING REQUIREMENT

Breed

One comparison has been made with three different breeds (Daghir and Balloun, 1963). The vitamin B$_6$ requirement to 4 weeks of age was determined for SCWL, RIR and Vantress × Arbor Acre chicks, using body weight, feed conversion, serum glutamic-oxalacetic transaminase (GOT) activity, incidence of gizzard erosion and gross clinical signs as criteria of adequacy. The serum GOT activity was less severely depressed by a low vitamin B$_6$ intake in SCWL than in either of the faster-growing breeds, but for optimal growth and feed conversion there was no difference in requirement which, for all three breeds, lay between 2·2 and 2·6 mg/kg.

Other dietary components

A vitamin B$_6$ deficiency induced by excess choline has been observed in broiler chicks by Saville, Solvyns and Humphries (1967). Birds given 1300 mg or more choline/kg diet in addition to the 660 mg/kg already present in the major ingredients showed signs of hyperexcitability, muscular inco-ordination and depression in growth at about six weeks of age. The condition was alleviated by administration of pyridoxine in the drinking water at a rate of 4 to 5 mg/litre. There is also a brief report (Fuller and Hill, 1964) that excess methionine accentuates the effects of vitamin B$_6$ deficiency.

Table 4.7
Water-soluble vitamin and choline requirements of fowls

	Preferred estimate of requirement mg/kg	Range of selected values	No. of values	Sources
Thiamin				
Chicks	1·0	0·7–1·4	5	1, 3, 37, 67, 68
Layers	1·25	0·7–1·25	2	52, 58
Breeders	?			
Riboflavin				
Chicks	4·0	3·0–7·2	6	8, 9, 10, 15, 32, 72
Layers	2.5	2·5–3·6	2	11, 54
Breeders	4·0	3·6–5·0	3	16, 33, 55
Nicotinic acid				
Chicks	28	25–33	4	13, 15, 24, 53
Layers	8	7·3–8·0	2	2, 59
Breeders	10	7·3–10·0	2	2, 59
Pantothenic acid				
Chicks	10	6–10	4	6, 7, 15, 38
Layers	1·5	1·0–1·5	2	7, 29
Breeders	6·5	6·5–8·0	4	5, 7, 29, 30
Pyridoxine				
Chicks	3·5	2·0–5·5	9	12, 23, 26, 27 34, 40, 41, 42, 45
Layers	2·0	2·0–2·3	2	20, 28
Breeders	4·0	2·0–5·5	3	20, 26, 28
Biotin				
Chicks	0·15	—	1	31
Layers	?			
Breeders	0·15	0·04–0·20	2	17, 19
Folic acid				
Chicks	1·5	0·6–2·0	4	35, 43, 47, 61
Layers	0·3	0·01–0·42	6	18, 21, 44, 63, 65, 66
Breeders	0·5	0·3–1·0	4	18, 21, 44, 65

Table 4.7—*continued*

	Preferred estimate of requirement mg/kg	Range of selected values	No. of values	Sources
Vitamin B_{12}				
Chicks	0·02*	0·015–0·027	2	51, 64
Layers	?			
Breeders	0·002	0·001–0·006	8	14, 36, 48, 50 56, 57, 70, 71
Choline				
Chicks	1300	1000–1900	7	25, 39, 46 49, 60, 62, 69
Layers	600	—	1	22
Breeders	1100	—	1	4

* Assuming negligible reserves at hatching.

Key to sources

1. Abbott *et al.* (1954)
2. Adams & Carrick (1967)
3. Arnold & Elvehjem (1938)
4. Balloun (1956)
5. Balloun & Phillips (1957)
6. Bauernfeind *et al.* (1942)
7. Beer *et al.* (1963)
8. Bethke & Record (1942)
9. Bolton (1944)
10. Bolton (1947)
11. Bolton (1959)
12. Briggs *et al.* (1942)
13. Childs *et al.* (1952)
14. Chin *et al.* (1958)
15. Coates *et al.* (1950)
16. Coles & Cumber (1955)
17. Couch *et al.* (1948)
18. Couch & German (1950)
19. Cravens *et al.* (1942)
20. Cravens *et al.* (1946)
21. Cravens & Halpin (1949)
22. Crawford *et al.* (1967)
23. Daghir & Balloun (1963)
24. Fisher *et al.* (1954)
25. Fritz *et al.* (1967)
26. Fuller & Field (1958)
27. Fuller & Kifer (1959)
28. Fuller *et al.* (1961)
29. Gillis *et al.* (1947)
30. Gillis *et al.* (1948)
31. Hegsted *et al.* (1942)
32. Heuser *et al.* (1938)
33. Hill *et al.* (1954)
34. Hogan *et al.* (1941)
35. Hutchings *et al.* (1946)
36. Johnson (1954)
37. Jukes & Heitman (1940)
38. Jukes & McElroy (1943)
39. Jukes & Stokstad (1951)
40. Kirchgessner & Friesecke (1963)
41. Kirchgessner & Maier (1968b)
42. Kratzer *et al.* (1947)
43. Lillie & Briggs (1947)
44. Lillie *et al.* (1950)
45. Maier & Kirchgessner (1967)
46. March & Biely (1956a)
47. March & Biely (1956b)
48. Mariakulandai & McGinnis (1953)
49. McKittrick (1947)
50. Milligan & Combs (1950)
51. Ott (1951)
52. Padhi & Combs (1950)
53. Patterson *et al.* (1956)
54. Petersen *et al.* (1947a)
55. Petersen *et al.* (1947b)
56. Petersen *et al.* (1952)
57. Petersen *et al.* (1953)
58. Polin *et al.* (1963)
59. Ringrose *et al.* (1965)
60. Roberts & Fritz (1968)
61. Robertson *et al.* (1946)
62. Schaefer *et al.* (1949)
63. Schweigert *et al.* (1948)
64. Stokstad *et al.* (1949)
65. Sunde *et al.* (1950)
66. Taylor (1947)
67. Thornton *et al.* (1957)
68. Thornton & Shutze (1960)
69. West *et al.* (1951)
70. Wiese *et al.* (1952)
71. Yacowitz *et al.* (1952)
72. Yoshida *et al.* (1966)

Table 4.8
Water-soluble vitamin and choline requirements of turkeys, ducks, geese and pheasants

	Preferred estimate of requirement mg/kg	Range of selected values	No. of values	Sources
Thiamin				
Turkey poult	2·0	1·0–2·0	2	20, 27
Breeding turkey	?			
Riboflavin				
Turkey poult	3·5	2·7–4·0	3	3, 19, 28
Breeding turkey	3·5	3·0–3·5	1	3
Duckling	4·0	—	1	8
Pheasant chick	3·5	—	1	24
Nicotinic acid				
Turkey poult	>20 <50	—	1	13
Breeding turkey	?			
Duckling	25	—	1	7
Gosling	65	—	1	2
Pheasant chick	60	50–70	2	24, 30
Pantothenic acid				
Turkey poult	10·5	—	1	17
Breeding turkey	16	—	1	15
Duckling	11	—	1	8
Pyridoxine				
Turkey poult	4·0	3·0–4·0	2	14, 29
Breeding turkey	?			
Duckling	2·5	—	1	9
Biotin				
Turkey poult	0·25	0·25	2	10, 31
Breeding turkey	0·2 (see text)			

Table 4.8—*(continued)*

	Preferred estimate of requirement mg/kg	Range of selected values	No. of values	Sources
Folic acid				
Turkey poult	1·5	0·8–2·0	4	13, 21, 22, 23
Breeding turkey	0·7	0·4–0·8	3	16, 18, 22
Vitamin B$_{12}$				
Turkey poult	0·004	0·002–0·010	2	11, 25
Breeding turkey	?			
Choline				
Turkey poult	1500	900–2500	6	4, 5, 6, 12, 26, 27
Breeding turkey	1350	1000–1700	2	1, 27
Pheasant chick	1400	—	1	24

Key to sources

1. Balloun & Miller (1964)
2. Battig *et al.* (1953)
3. Boucher *et al.* (1942)
4. Evans (1943)
5. Gartley *et al.* (1951)
6. Gogus & Griminger (1957)
7. Hegsted (1946)
8. Hegsted & Perry (1948)
9. Hegsted & Rao (1945)
10. Jensen & Martinson (1969)
11. Johnson (1955)
12. Jukes (1940)
13. Jukes *et al.* (1947)
14. Kratzer *et al.* (1947)
15. Kratzer *et al.* (1955)
16. Kratzer *et al.* (1956)
17. Kratzer & Williams (1948)
18. Miller & Balloun (1967)
19. Patrick *et al.* (1944)
20. Robenalt (1960)
21. Russell *et al.* (1947)
22. Schweigert *et al.* (1948)
23. Scott *et al.* (1948)
24. Scott *et al.* (1959)
25. Sherwood & Briggs (1951)
26. Sherwood & Sloan (1954)
27. Singsen *et al.* (1950)
28. Slinger *et al.* (1955)
29. Sullivan *et al.* (1967)
30. Sunde & Bird (1957)
31. Waibel *et al.* (1969)

BIOTIN

In young birds deprived of biotin, growth rate is diminished and a scaly dermatitis develops under the feet, which later become cracked and bleeding. There is some incidence of perosis and "parrot beak". Leg weakness and enlarged hocks in turkey poults have been attributed to biotin deficiency (Scott, 1968; Jensen and Martinson, 1969). Biotin is essential for normal embryo development. Hatchability of eggs from hens deprived of biotin falls rapidly. There are two peak periods of embryo mortality, one during the first week of incubation and another in the last three days (Cravens, McGibbon and Sebesta, 1944). Among the hatched chicks there is a high incidence of congenital perosis, ataxia and skeletal deformities (Couch, Cravens, Elvehjem and Halpin, 1948).

ASSESSMENT OF REQUIREMENT

There have been few recent quantitative attempts to determine the biotin requirements of chickens. An estimated requirement by the growing chick of 0·09 mg/kg (Wagstaff, Dobson and Anderson, 1961) proved inadequate in later studies. The higher value of 0·15 mg/kg (Anderson and Warnick, 1970) has been chosen. A figure for the breeding hen estimated from the data of Cravens, Sebesta, Halpin and Hart (1942) and Couch *et al.* (1948) has been entered in the table, but it is clear that the question of the biotin requirements of the fowl needs considerably more investigation.

In the past few years several reported field cases of biotin deficiency have revived interest in its importance in turkey nutrition. Two recent extensive trials indicate that the requirement of poults during the first few weeks of life is of the order of 0·25 mg/kg (Jensen and Martinson, 1969; Waibel, Krista, Arnold, Blaylock and Neagle, 1969) and this value has been entered in the table in preference to the older, and slightly lower, estimate of Patrick, Boucher, Dutcher and Knandel (1942). Waibel *et al.* (1969) found 0·15 mg biotin/kg to be adequate for breeding turkey hens but this could be an underestimate since the birds were maintained on litter and might have obtained part of their requirement from microbially synthesized biotin in the droppings. A figure of 0·2 mg/kg has therefore been tentatively suggested in the table.

FACTORS AFFECTING THE REQUIREMENT

Biotin is present in cereals in a bound form that is not fully utilized by the bird. In studies with chicks it proved less available from wheat and barley than from oats or maize (Wagstaff, Dobson and Anderson, 1961). Fish meals and meat and bone meals also appeared to contain biotin that was not fully utilized by the chick (Anderson and Warnick, 1970). The presence of rancid fats in the diet may cause destruction of biotin. For these reasons Scott (1968) recommends addition of 0·08 to 0·10 mg/kg to practical starting diets for turkeys, and the same amount to turkey breeder diets to ensure a good carry-over of biotin to the newly hatched poult.

---

[1]It has recently been reported that the fatty liver and kidney syndrome (FLKS) of chicks involves biotin deficiency as a major contributing factor and that biotin supplementation of susceptible diets effectively prevents FLKS (Payne, Gilchrist, Pearson and Hemsley, 1974: *Br. Poult. Sci.* **15**, 489).

FOLIC ACID

The term "folic acid" refers to a class of substances the simplest of which is pteroylmonoglutamic acid (PGA). This compound can by synthesized chemically and is used as a supplement in poultry diets. Most of the folic acid in natural feedstuffs is present in the form of polyglutamates, in which the PGA is conjugated with further molecules of glutamic acid. It is not known whether these conjugated forms are as readily available to higher animals as the simple monoglutamate.

EFFECTS OF DEPRIVATION

Folic acid is essential for maturation of the red blood cells, hence a macrocytic anaemia is characteristic of its deficiency. In addition, young chicks and poults grow and feather poorly and have a high incidence of perosis. Feather pigmentation may be abnormal. Cervical paralysis has been reported in poults deprived of folic acid. Inadequate intake by breeding birds results in very poor hatchability of their eggs, and egg production is reduced in severe deficiency.

ASSESSMENT OF REQUIREMENT

The requirement of turkey breeder hens for folic acid has been recently reassessed, using diets of natural ingredients (Miller and Balloun, 1967). The natural folic acid content of the basal diet, 0·35 mg/kg, was adequate for egg production, egg fertility and optimal feed conversion, but did not support maximal hatchability. The requirement for good hatchability on a diet containing adequate choline (1350 mg/kg) was 0·81 mg/kg. The value given in Table 4.8 has therefore been increased to 0·7 mg/kg, the median of this last estimate and the two previously published (Schweigert, German, Pearson and Sherwood, 1948; Kratzer, Davis and Abbott, 1956). There has been no modification of estimates for other classes of poultry.

FACTORS AFFECTING REQUIREMENT

Choline

Since folic acid is concerned in the synthesis of labile methyl groups it is to be expected that the requirements for folic acid and choline are interrelated. In the presence of adequate choline Young, Norris and Heuser (1955) found the young chick's requirement for folic acid to be about 0·46 mg/kg, but in the absence of choline it was increased to 0·96 mg/kg. High levels of folic acid, however, could not compensate for a deficiency of choline. Similarly in breeding turkeys Miller and Balloun (1967) reported an increased need for folic acid from 0·81 mg/kg on a diet with 1375 mg choline/kg to at least 1·67 mg/kg on a diet with inadequate choline.

Fat

There is some evidence that high levels of fat increase the bird's requirement for folic acid. March and Biely (1955) considered that the quality of the fat was important and only noted an increased folic acid requirement of chicks given 5% extra dietary fat if the fat had been severely heated. In turkey breeder hens addition to the diet of 5% soya bean oil depressed egg fertility and hatchability, even in the presence of 1·67 mg folic acid/kg (Miller and Balloun, 1967).

127

Protein

March and Biely (1956b) reported that the folic acid requirement of the chick was increased on diets high in protein or fat or both. The effect of high protein diets on folic acid requirement was confirmed by Creek, and Vasaitis (1963) in a series of trails with a semi-purified diet adequate in choline and vitamin B_{12}. Increasing the protein content to 1·5 times that of the basal diet led to depression in growth and increased incidence of perosis. Growth was restored and the incidence of perosis considerably reduced by an extra supplement of 0·30 mg folic acid/kg.

VITAMIN B_{12}

Vitamin B_{12} is produced commercially by a fermentation process. The most stable product, and the material commonly used as a dietary supplement, is cyanocobalamin. Compounds are known in which the cyano- group is replaced by other anions, and these have similar biological properties.

EFFECTS OF DEPRIVATION

Young birds deprived of vitamin B_{12} grow and feather poorly and mortality is high although the exact cause of death is not known. Kidney damage and perosis have been reported among the signs of deficiency. Adult birds show few effects, but the eggs they produce fail to hatch. Peak embryo mortality usually occurs during the second and third weeks of incubation. The dead-in-shell embryos are dwarfed, with myoatrophy of the legs, enlarged hearts and thyroids, multiple haemorrhages throughout the organs and fatty livers (Ferguson, Rigdon and Couch, 1955). Failure in myelination of the sciatic nerves has been observed histochemically (Alexander, 1957).

ASSESSMENT OF REQUIREMENT

For most classes of poultry the "physiological" requirement for vitamin B_{12} is not precisely known. In nature vitamin B_{12} is synthesized by micro-organisms in poultry droppings, fermented food or drinking water contaminated with food residues. It is therefore easy for the bird to acquire the minute amount of the vitamin required to satisfy its needs. Furthermore, considerable reserves are carried over from dam to offspring in the egg. An acute deficiency of vitamin B_{12} is thus only encountered under laboratory conditions. Studies of this kind with the fowl have established that 0·02 mg vitamin B_{12}/kg diet is required in the absence of significant "carry-over" from the egg or any extraneous contribution from microbial sources. In more practical conditions it is doubtful whether a dietary source of the vitamin is necessary at all, and a supplement of 0·001 to 0·002 mg/kg is more than adequate in most circumstances.

FACTORS AFFECTING REQUIREMENT

Management

Birds of all classes managed on deep litter obtain ample supples of vitamin B_{12} from the products of microbial synthesis in the litter. Breeding birds maintained on clean wire floors are likely eventually to exhaust their tissue stores carried over from the egg and will require a dietary supply of vitamin B_{12}, particularly in view of its importance in hatching.

128

Other dietary components

Vitamin B_{12} is involved in the synthesis of methionine from homocystine in the tissues and hence the two substances may have a mutually sparing action, although neither can replace the other (Langer and Kratzer, 1964). There is a similar relationship between dietary choline and vitamin B_{12}, although choline is less effective than methionine in sparing the vitamin (Briggs, Hill and Giles, 1950). Although it is not possible from the available data to give quantitative guidance, it should be borne in mind that on diets low in methionine or choline the need for dietary vitamin B_{12} will probably be increased. The interrelationship between vitamin B_{12} and pantothenic acid has already been discussed (see page 122).

ASCORBIC ACID

Ascorbic acid is not usually considered an essential vitamin for poultry since most birds are capable of synthesizing it in sufficient quantity to cover their metabolic needs in normal circumstances. It appears, however, that in certain conditions of "stress" the demand for ascorbic acid becomes greater than can be provided for by tissue synthesis, and a dietary supplement may be beneficial. Some instances of improved performance as a result of ascorbic acid supplementation are given below.

High energy diets

March and Biely (1953) studied the effects of supplements of aureomycin and ascorbic acid to high-energy diets for New Hampshire chicks. The extra energy was supplied as maize starch, tallow or herring oil. The antibiotic increased growth rate by about 2% on the diets with starch and herring oil; on all diets the antibiotic combined with 2 g ascorbic acid/kg produced a 5% improvement in growth. However, on a purified diet with an ME content of about 3·9 Mcal (16·3 MJ)/kg Gogus and Griminger (1959) observed no enhancement of growth of broiler chicks when the diet was supplemented with 0·2g ascorbic acid/kg.

Climatic stress

Exposure to extremes of temperature can have adverse effects on fertility and general health of poultry. There are several examples of beneficial results from dietary supplements of ascorbic acid in birds kept at high temperatures. In experiments made in Israel (Perek and Snapir, 1963), semen production of White Rock cocks was significantly improved by addition of 100 mg ascorbic acid/kg diet. In similar studies with WL hens (Perek and Kendler, 1963) egg yields, egg weight, cull and mortality rates were all improved by dietary supplements of up to 400 mg ascorbic acid/kg. In the USA ascorbic acid at a level of 22 mg/kg prevented the decline in shell strength usually experienced during the summer months, but did not improve egg production, size or internal quality (Thornton and Moreng, 1959). The beneficial effect of ascorbic acid in maintaining shell thickness at elevated environmental temperatures was confirmed by Thornton (1960b) using a diet containing 130 g protein/kg. However, on a similar diet with 170 g protein/kg the reverse was true and the ascorbic acid supplement proved significantly detrimental.

Disease

Reduced blood levels of vitamin C have been reported in birds suffering from a variety of diseases, including *pullorum* disease, fowl typhoid and intestinal parasitic infestations (Satterfield, Moseley, Gauger, Holmes and Trip, 1940). This has led to investigations of the possible role of ascorbic acid in defence against infection. Although high dietary supplements of all vitamins, including 1 g ascorbic acid/kg, have been shown to reduce mortality rate in experimentally induced fowl typhoid (Hill, Garren, Kelly and Barber, 1955) and lymphomatosis (Hill and Garren, 1957a) there is still no very conclusive evidence that dietary vitamin C significantly affects the course of the common diseases of poultry.

CHOLINE

EFFECTS OF DEPRIVATION

One of the main reasons for the importance of choline as an ingredient in poultry diets is to provide a source of labile methyl groups, but this property is shared by other methylating agents including methionine. Choline is itself synthesized in animal tissues from simpler compounds. Although there are reports that diets low in choline support poor growth and feed conversion in young birds, and reduced egg size and hatchability in adults, these effects seem mainly to reflect deficiency of a dietary source of methyl groups or of the vitamins concerned in their synthesis (see below). However, choline appears to play a specific role in the prevention of perosis.

ASSESSMENT OF REQUIREMENT

The previous values have been reassessed in the light of more recent work. For the young chick the best estimate of requirement is still 1300 mg/kg, with a range of 1000 to 1900 mg/kg. This is based on seven investigations (listed in Table 4.7) and supported by Deeb and Thornton (1959). Several authors state that the amount needed to sustain optimal growth is less than that required completely to prevent perosis. All values are based on work with diets containing adequate methionine and vitamin B_{12}.

There is no recent work on the quantitative requirements of turkey poults for choline, but the results of Slinger, Pepper and Sibbald (1962) suggest that the previous estimate of 1500 mg/kg is adequate. For breeding hens the value of 1100 mg/kg (Balloun, 1956) has not been superseded, but for layers a lower level of 600 mg/kg has recently been indicated (Crawford, Griffith, Teekell and Watts, 1967). A brief report by Singsen, Matterson, Kozeff and Decker (1950) indicated that although about 1200 mg choline/kg was adequate for good hatchability of turkey eggs, better poult weights were obtained if the breeders had received 1700 mg/kg. In a more extensive study by Balloun and Miller (1964) not more than 1000 mg/kg was necessary in a medium-energy, practical-type diet for the maintenance of egg production, hatchability, and growth and viability of the poults. A mean of these two values has been given in Table 4.8.

FACTORS AFFECTING REQUIREMENT

The two major dietary components that influence the bird's need for a dietary source of choline are methionine and vitamin B_{12}. If the amount of methionine in the diet is only just sufficient to meet the needs for protein synthesis, there is then a higher demand for choline as a methyl donor. According to McKittrick (1947) the growing chick requires 5 g methionine and 1 g choline/kg of diet plus either 2·5 g methionine or 4.5 g choline/kg or any equivalent combination of the two. Vitamin B_{12} is essential for the *de novo* synthesis of methyl groups in animal tissue and hence, in its absence, the supply of labile methyl groups from choline becomes critical. Schaefer *et al.* (1949) and Jukes and Stokstad (1951) both demonstrated that the choline requirement of growing chicks was markedly reduced by supplementation with vitamin B_{12}, but the latter authors noted that the amount of choline required to prevent perosis was not decreased by supplying vitamin B_{12}. High levels of fat in the diet have been shown to increase the chick's need for dietary choline but, as March and Biely (1956a) point out, this is probably secondary to an increased use of methionine for protein synthesis. In such circumstances it has been estimated that 1 g choline is equivalent to 2·3 to 2·4 g DL-methionine as a methyl donor (Quillin, Combs, Creek and Romoser, 1961).

EFFECTS OF EXCESS

There are some indications that high levels of choline may be detrimental. For instance Deeb and Thornton (1959) found that quantities of more than 2200 mg/kg slightly depressed body weight. Saville, Solvyns and Humphries (1967) observed reduced weight and signs typical of vitamin B_6 deficiency at about six weeks of age in chicks given diets containing more than 2000 mg choline/kg. The condition could be alleviated by administration of pyridoxol or by withdrawal of choline from the diet.

ESSENTIAL FATTY ACIDS

The most important essential fatty acids (EFAs) are linoleic and arachidonic acids, neither of which can be synthesized *de novo* by poultry. However, the bird can derive arachidonic acid from linoleic acid and hence the total requirement for EFAs is usually expressed in terms of linoleic acid.

EFFECTS OF DEPRIVATION

Most experimental work indicates that retarded growth is associated with EFA deficiency in chicks (reviewed by Balnave, 1970b) although Hill (1966) has shown that growth rate is a poor criterion for assessing EFA deficiency in chicks. Fatty liver development and increased liver size have been observed by a number of workers (Edwards, Marion and Driggers, 1962; Edwards, 1967; Hopkins and Nesheim, 1967). Bieri, Briggs, Fox, Pollard and Ortiz (1956) have observed increased water consumption in EFA deficiency.

Ross and Adamson (1961) indicated that EFAs might play an important function in relation to disease resistance and other workers have confirmed a reduced resistance to disease in EFA-deficient chicks (Hopkins and Nesheim, 1962a; Hopkins, Witter and Nesheim, 1963; Boyd and Edwards, 1966; Edwards, 1967).

Bieri *et al.* (1956, 1957) noted that EFA deficiency produced smaller testes in male chicks, an observation also made by Edwards (1963a, 1967). Edwards (1967) also noted that EFA-deficient male chicks did not develop normal secondary sexual characteristics. Edwards (1967) and Lillie and Menge (1968) have reported that EFA deficiency significantly reduces the fertilising capacity of the adult cockerel.

Adult animals are difficult to deplete of EFAs because of the large reservoir of linoleate in adipose tissue. Therefore, unless animals are reared on diets low in linoleic acid, symptoms of an EFA deficiency may not be observed even after prolonged feeding of a linoleate-deficient diet (Miller, Menge and Denton, 1963;

Calvert, 1965; Balnave and Brown, 1968). As it is so difficult to deplete poultry of their EFA reserves, most studies carried out to estimate the dietary requirements of laying hens for EFAs have utilized birds which were reared on linoleic acid-deficient diets and few comparisons have been made with birds maintained throughout on a conventional diet. In experiments where birds were maintained on conventional or semi-purified low-fat diets prior to receiving dietary EFAs the beneficial effects of linoleic acid were relatively much smaller.

EFA deficiency in hens is characterised by reductions in egg products, egg size, fertility and hatchability of fertile eggs, A decreased body weight, and increased mortality are also observed in EFA-deficient birds. However, there appears to be a higher quantitative requirement of linoleic acid for the maintenance of maximum egg size than for egg production, fertility and hatchability.

ASSESSMENT OF REQUIREMENT

An increase in eicosatrienoic acid in certain tissues has been observed in EFA-deficient animals and this has been used as an indication of EFA deficiency. The ratio of eicosatrienoic acid to arachidonic acid in tissue lipids has been used to estimate the EFA requirement of the chick. Hill (1966) has estimated the linoleate requirement of the chick to be about 8 g/kg of diet, while Bieri and Prival (1966) have estimated the requirement as between 4 and 8 g/kg of diet. Hill, Silbernick and McMeans (1967) have also obtained a figure of 8 g/kg of diet. Hopkins and Nesheim (1967) using chicks obtained from hens fed diets low in linoleic acid estimated the requirement as about 8 g/kg. However, using growth and liver composition as a reference guide these latter workers estimated the linoleic acid requirement to be 14 g/kg of diet. Menge (1970) reported that the linoleate requirements of male and female chickens to 6 weeks of age are approximately 12 g and 6 g linoleic acid/kg of diet. It therefore appears that the linoleic acid requirement of normal chicks probably does not exceed 10 g/kg of diet.

Estimated requirements of the adult hen are given in Table 4.9. It appears from these data that a dietary level of 20 g linoleate/kg would be sufficient to satisfy all requirements, although as these birds were maintained over an extended period on diets containing abnormally low levels of linoleic acid it is probable that, for birds fed conventional diets, the requirements would be much lower than those quoted in Table 4.9. This can be confirmed by calculating the linoleic acid content of conventional rations without added oil. Such calculations indicate that practical diets based on maize contain approximately 13 to 16 g linoleic acid/kg. Diets containing little or no maize would contain even less linoleate. In experiments where a conventional diet was fed either prior to the experiment or as the experimental basal diet it has not always been possible to show a beneficial effect of supplementary linoleate on reproduction (Edwards, 1963b; Balnave, 1970a), showing that the amount of linoleate stored during the growing period has an important effect on the subsequent EFA requirement.

In laying hens, the character which shows the greatest requirement for linoleate is egg weight. Figure 4.1 indicates the response in egg weight to varying levels of dietary linoleic acid supplied from cereals or vegetable oils. The data indicate that, for birds previously maintained over an extended period on diets containing abnormally low levels of linoleic acid, maximum egg size can usually be attained with approximately 20 to 25 g linoleate/kg of diet. However, when birds have been maintained on conventional rations the requirement is considerably reduced and maximum egg size can usually be attained with approximately 12 g linoleate/kg of diet. Therefore, although the linoleate content of conventional diets would appear to be satisfactory for fertility and hatch-

Table 4.9
Linoleic acid requirements of laying hens depleted prior to experiment

Source	Depletion period	Experimental period	Linoleic acid in basal diet mg/kg	Source of linoleic acid	Linoleic acid requirement (mg/bird day, unless otherwise stated)			
					Maximum egg production	Maximum egg size	80 per cent production of fertile eggs	80 per cent hatchability of fertile eggs
Menge, Calvert & Denton (1965a)	Day old to 25 weeks	5 months	50	Safflower oil	250	250	10	>250
Menge, Calvert & Denton (1965b)	Day old to 32 weeks	5 months	50	Safflower oil	1600	1600	5	>1600
Menge (1968)	2 to 22 weeks	20 weeks	20	Maize oil	3500	1800	2	400
Balnave (1969)	Day old to 35 weeks	12 weeks	3500	Maize oil	750	750	—	—
Balnave & Brown (1968)	12 to 48 weeks	12 weeks	3000	Maize oil	10–20 g/kg diet	20–40 g/kg diet	—	—

ability some benefit in egg size may be obtained from dietary supplementation with linoleic acid, especially with diets containing wheat or barley as the sole cereal ingredients.

Cooper and Barnett (1968) fed a practical breeder diet containing 12 g linoleate/kg and an isocaloric diet containing 38 g linoleate/kg to turkey breeder hens and found no significant difference in body weight, egg production, hatchability of fertile eggs or feed consumption although there was a significant increase in egg weight in birds fed the higher level of linoleic acid.

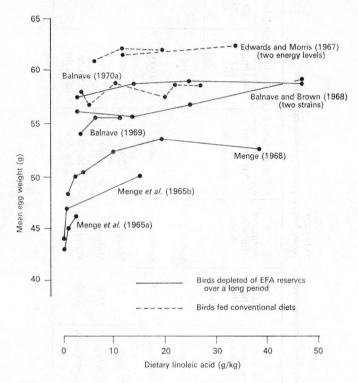

Fig. 4.1. The response in egg weight obtained by including different levels of linoleic acid in iso-energetic diets fed *ad libitum*.

FACTORS AFFECTING REQUIREMENT

Other dietary fats

There is some evidence to suggest that oils of marine origin have a beneficial effect on reproductive performance that cannot be attributed solely to their EFA content (Menge, Calvert and Denton, 1965b). In this work it appeared that the linoleate requirement was considerably reduced in the presence of long-chain polyunsaturated fatty acids from menhaden oil. However, this effect of marine oils has not always been verified by experimentation (Marion and Edwards, 1964; Balnave, 1969, 1970c) and it may be that the effect is only evident when there is a severe deficiency of EFA in the diet.

134

Dietary energy

The beneficial response in egg production and egg size resulting from feeding vegetable oils has normally been attributed to the EFA content of those oils but the results of some experimental work have suggested that these effects are more likely due to the increased energy concentration of the diet (Shutze, Jensen and McGinnis, 1962; Harms and Waldroup, 1963; Blamberg, Bossard and Combs, 1964). However, the experimental findings of such workers as Bray (1967), Edwards and Morris (1967) and Menge (1968) indicate that linoleic acid *per se* has a significant influence on egg size. Recent work has indicated that there is not a simple relationship between energy intake and linoleate supplementation of a diet and that once the requirement for linoleic acid has been met other factors such as amino acid balance, protein intake or metabolizable energy may be responsible for increased reproductive performance (Menge, Calvert and Denton, 1965a; Balnave, 1969). This has been verified by Balnave (1971) who has recently shown that although dietary supplementation with maize oil improves egg size in birds fed conventional rations the total egg yield is similar to that of birds fed equivalent levels of metabolizable energy from maize starch.

Maternal diet

There is considerable evidence to suggest that maternal diet is important in the subsequent growth of chicks and affects their requirement for dietary EFA (Hopkins and Nesheim, 1962a, b, 1967; Edwards, 1963b, 1967; Menge, Miller and Denton, 1964; Menge and Richardson, 1968).

REFERENCES

ABBOTT, O. J., BIRD, H. R. & CRAVENS, W. W. (1954). *Poult. Sci.* **33**, 1245
ABBOTT, U. K, McMARTIN, D. A., ADLER, H. E. & KRATZER, F. H. (1960). *Poult. Sci.* **39**. 315
ADAMS, R. L. & CARRICK, C. W. (1967). *Poult. Sci.* **46**, 712
ALEXANDER, W. F. (1957). In *Vitamin B₁₂ und Intrinsik Faktor.* Ed. H. C. Heinrich. Stuttgart, Enke
ALMQUIST, H. J. (1954). In *The vitamins* **2**, 419. Ed. W. H. Sebrell & R. S. Harris. New York, Academic Press
ALMQUIST, H. J. & STOKSTAD, E. L. R. (1936). *J. Nutr.* **12**, 329
AMES, S. R. (1956). *Poult Sci.* **35**, 145
ANDERSON, J. O. & WARNICK, R. E. (1970). *Poult. Sci.* **49**, 569
ARNOLD, A. & ELVEHJEM, C. A. (1938). *J. Nutr.* **15**, 403
ARSCOTT, G. H. & PARKER, J. E. (1967). *J. Nutr.* **91**, 219
ARSCOTT, G. H., PARKER, J. E. & DICKINSON, E. M. (1965). *J. Nutr.* **87**, 63
ASCARELLI, I. (1957). *Poult. Sci.* **36**, 549
ASCARELLI, I. & BARTOV, I. (1963). *Poult. Sci.* **42**, 232
ASCARELLI, I. & BONDI, A. (1957). *J. agric, Sci., Camb.* **49**, 113
ATKINSON, R. L., FERGUSON, T. M., QUISENBERRY, J. H. & COUCH, J. R. (1955). *J. Nutr.* **55**, 387
BAKER, J. R., HOWELL, J.McC. & THOMPSON, J. N. (1967). *Br. J. exp. Path.* **48**, 507
BALLOUN, S. L. (1956). *Poult. Sci.* **35**, 737
BALLOUN, S. L. & MILLER, D. L. (1964). *Poult. Sci.* **43**, 64

BALLOUN, S. L. & PHILLIPS, R. E. (1957). *Poult. Sci.* **36,** 929
BALNAVE, D. (1969). *J. Sci. Fd Agric.* **20,** 556
BALNAVE, D. (1970a). *Poult. Sci.* **49,** 1197
BALNAVE, D. (1970b). *Wld's Poult. Sci. J.* **26,** 442
BALNAVE, D. (1970c). *Rec. agric. Res. Minist. Agric. Nth Ir.* **18,** 71
BALNAVE, D. (1971). *J. Sci. Fd Agric.* **22,** 125
BALNAVE, D. & BROWN, W. O. (1968). *Poult. Sci.* **47,** 1212
BATTIG, M. J., HILL, E. G., CANFIELD, T. H. & SLOAN, H. J. (1953). *Poult. Sci.* **32.** 550
BAUERNFEIND, J. C., NORRIS, L. C. & HEUSER, G. F. (1942). *Poult. Sci.* **21,** 142
BEARSE, G. E., MCCLARY, C. F. & SAXENA, H. C. (1960). *Poult. Sci.* **39,** 860
BEER, A. E., SCOTT, M. L. & NESHEIM, M. C. (1963). *Br. Poult. Sci.* **4,** 243
BETHKE, R. M. & RECORD, P. R. (1942). *Poult. Sci.* **21,** 147
BETHKE, R. M., RECORD, P. R., WILDER, O. H. M. & KENNARD, D. C. (1937). *Poult. Sci.* **16,** 438
BIELY, J. & MARCH, B. E. (1967). *Poult. Sci.* **46,** 223
BIELY, J., WOOD, J. D. & TOPLIFF, J. E. (1962). *Poult. Sci.* **41,** 1175
BIERI, J. G., BRIGGS, G. M., SPIVEY FOX, M. R., POLLARD, C. J. & ORTIZ, L. O. (1956). *Proc. Soc. exp. Biol. Med.* **93,** 237
BIERI, J. G., POLLARD, C. J. & BRIGGS, G. M. (1957). *Archs Biochem. Biophys.* **68,** 300
BIERI, J. G. & PRIVAL, E. L. (1966). *J. Nutr.* **90,** 428
BIRD, H. R., CULTON, T. G. & KLINE, O. L. (1940). *J. Nutr.* **19:** suppl., 15
BLACK, D. J. G. & COATES, M. E. (1948). *Proc. 8th Wld's Poult. Congr.* **1,** 96
BLAMBERG, D. L., BOSSARD, E. H. & COMBS, G. F. (1964). *Poult. Sci.* **43,** 1304
BOLTON, W. F. (1944). *J. agric. Sci., Camb.* **34,** 198
BOLTON, W. F. (1947). *J. agric. Sci., Camb.* **37,** 316
BOLTON, W. F. (1959). *J. agric. Sci., Camb.* **52,** 364
BOUCHER, R. V., PATRICK, H. & KNANDEL, H. C. (1942). *Poult. Sci.* **21,** 466
BOYD, F. M. & EDWARDS, H. M. (1962). *Poult. Sci.* **41,** 750
BOYD, F. M. & EDWARDS, H. M. (1966). *Proc. Soc. exp. Biol. Med.* **122,** 218
BRAY, D. J. (1967). *Poult. Sci.* **46,** 476
BRIGGS, G. M., HILL, E. G. & GILES, M. J. (1950). *Poult. Sci.* **29,** 723
BRIGGS, G. M., MILLS, R. C., HEGSTED, D. M., ELVEHJEM, C. A. & HART, E. B. (1942). *Poult. Sci.* **21,** 379
BRUBACHER, G., FRIESECKE, H., STREIFF, K. & WISS, O. (1959). *Int. Z. VitamForsch.* **30,** 213
BRUBACHER, G., GLOOR, U., WISS. O., WÜRSCH, J. & TAGWERKER, F. (1962). *Proc. 12th Wld's Poult. Congr.,* 164
BUNNELL, R. H., MATTERSON, L. D., SINGSEN, E. P. & EATON, H. D. (1956). *Poult. Sci.* **35,** 436
CALVERT, C. C. (1965). *Proc. Cornell Nutr. Conf. Fd Mfrs,* 104
CARLSON, C. W., MCGINNIS, J. & JENSEN, L. S. (1964). *J. Nutr.* **82,** 366
CARLSON, C. W., SAXENA, H. C., JENSEN, L. S. & MCGINNIS, J. (1964). *J. Nutr.* **82,** 507
CARVER, J. S., EVANS, R. J. & MCGINNIS, J. (1946). *Poult. Sci.* **25,** 294
CHAVEZ, R., CREGER, C. R. & COUCH, J. R. (1963). *Poult. Sci.* **42,** 1259
CHEN, P. S. & BOSMANN, H. B. (1964). *J. Nutr.* **83,** 133
CHEN, P. S. & BOSMANN, H. B. (1965). *J. Nutr.* **87,** 148
CHILDS, G. R., CARRICK, C. W. & HAUGE, S. M. (1952). *Poult. Sci.* **31,** 551
CHIN, D., ANDERSON, J. B., MILLER, R. F., NORRIS, L. C. & HEUSER, G. F. (1958). *Poult. Sci.* **37,** 335
CIPERA, J. D. (1967). *Can. J. Biochem.* **45,** 729
CIPERA, J. D. & WILLMER, W. S. (1963). *Can. J. Biochem, Physiol.* **41,** 1490
COATES, M. E. & HARRISON, G. F. (1957). *Proc. Nutr. Soc.* **16,** xxi
COATES, M. E., KON, S. K. & SHEPHEARD, E. E. (1950). *Br. J. Nutr.* **4,** 203
COLES, B., BIELY, J. & MARCH, B. E. (1970). *Poult. Sci.* **49,** 671
COLES, R. & CUMBER, F. (1955). *J. agric. Sci., Camb.* **46,** 191
COOPER, J. B. & BARNETT, B. D. (1968). *Poult. Sci.* **47,** 671
CORRELL, J. T. & WISE, E. C. (1938). *J. biol. Chem.* **126,** 573
COUCH, J. R., CRAVENS, W. W., ELVEHJEM, C. A. & HALPIN, J. G. (1948). *Anat. Rec.* **100,** 29
COUCH, J. P. & GERMAN, H. L. (1950), *Poult. Sci.* **29,** 539
COVER, M. S., MELLEN, W. J. & GILL, E. (1955). *Cornell Vet.* **45,** 366

CRAVENS, W. W. & HALPIN, J. G. (1949). *J. Nutr.* **37**, 127
CRAVENS, W. W., McGIBBON, W. H. & SEBESTA, E. E. (1944). *Anat, Rec.* **90**, 55
CRAVENS, W. W., SEBESTA, E. E., HALPIN, J. G. & HART, E. B. (1942). *Proc. Soc. exp. Biol. Med.* **50**, 101
CRAVENS, W. W., SEBESTA, E. E., HALPIN, J. G. & HART, E. B. (1946). *Poult, Sci.* **25**, 80
CRAWFORD, J. S., GRIFFITH, M., TEEKELL, R. A. & WATTS, A. B. (1967). *Poult. Sci.* **46**, 1249
CREEK, R. D. & VASAITIS, V. (1963). *Poult. Sci.* **42**, 1136
DAGHIR, N. J. & BALLOUN, S. L. (1963). *J. Nutr.* **79**, 279
DAM, H., PRANGE, I. & SØNDERGAARD, E. (1952). *Acta path, microbiol. scand,* **31**, 172
DAM, H. & SØNDERGAARD, E. (1964). *Z. ErnährWiss.* **5**, 73
DAVIES, M. K., GREGORY, M. E. & HENRY, K. M. (1959). *J. Dairy Res.* **26**, 215
DEEB, S. S. & THORNTON, P. A. (1959). *Poult. Sci.* **38**, 1198
DENTON, A. E. & BIELANSKI, E. R. (1958). *J. agric. Fd Chem.* **6**, 853
DEUEL, H. J. (1957). In *The lipids,* **3**, 681. New York, Wiley
DONOVAN, G. A. (1965a). *Poult. Sci.* **44**, 1292
DONOVAN, G. A. (1965b). *Poult. Sci.* **44**, 1365
DONOVAN, G. A., HENDERSON, D. C. & LUNEAU, R. N. (1961). *Poult. Sci.* **40**, 1395
DUA, P. N. & DAY, E. J. (1964). *Poult. Sci.* **43**, 1511
DUA, P. N. & DAY, E. J. (1966). *Poult. Sci.* **45**, 94
DUA, P. N., TIPON, H. C. & DAY, E. J. (1965). *Poult. Sci.* **44**, 1365
EDWARDS, D. G. & MORRIS, T. R. (1967). *Br. Poult. Sci.* **8**, 163
EDWARDS, H. M. (1963a). *Poult. Sci.* **42**, 1266
EDWARDS, H. M. (1963b). *Proc. Cornell Nutr. Conf. Fd Mfrs,* 93
EDWARDS, H. M. (1967). *Poult. Sci.* **46**, 1128
EDWARDS, H. M., MARION, J. E. & DRIGGERS, J. C. (1962). *Proc. 12th Wld's Poult. Congr.* 182
ELY, C. M. (1959). *Poult. Sci.* **38**, 1316
ERASMUS, J., SCOTT, M. L. & LEVINE, P. P. (1960). *Poult. Sci.* **39**, 565
EVANS, R. J. (1943). *Poult. Sci.* **22**, 266
EVANS, R. J., CARVER, J. S. & WILHELM, L. A. (1944). *Poult. Sci.* **23**, 234
FERGUSON, T. M., RIGDON, R. H. & COUCH, J. R. (1955). *Archs Path.* **60**, 393
FISHER, H., SCOTT, H. M. & JOHNSON, B. C. (1954). *Poult. Sci.* **33**, 1054
FRITZ, J. C., ARCHER, W. & BARKER, D. (1941). *Poult. Sci.* **20**, 545
FRITZ, J. C., ROBERTS, T. & BOEHNE, J. W. (1967). *Poult. Sci.* **46**, 1447
FROST, D. V., PERDUE, H. S. & SPRUTH, H. C. (1956). *J. Nutr.* **59**, 181
FRY, J. L., WALDROUP, P. W., DAMRON, B. L., HARMS, R. H. & WILSON, H. R. (1968). *Poult. Sci.* **47**, 630
FULLER, H. L. & FIELD, R. C. (1958). *Poult. Sci.* **37**, 1206
FULLER, H. L., FIELD, R. C., RONCALLI-AMICI, R., DUNAHOO, W. S. & EDWARDS, H. M. (1961). *Poult. Sci.* **40**, 249
FULLER, H. L. & HILL, R. L. (1964). *Poult. Sci.* **43**, 1320
FULLER, H. L. & KIFER, R. C. (1959). *Poult. Sci.* **38**, 255
GARTLEY, K. M., SLINGER, S. J., MORPHET, A. M. & CAMERON, C. R. (1951). *Poult. Sci.* **30**, 913
GEHLE, M. H. & BALLOUN, S. L. (1965). *J. Nutr.* **87**, 197
GERRIETS, E. (1961). *Br. vet. J.* **117**, 507
GERRIETS, E. (1966). *Berl. Münch, tierärztl. Wschr.* **79**, 271
GILLIS, M. B., HEUSER, G. F. & NORRIS, L. C. (1947). *Poult. Sci.* **26**, 540
GILLIS, M. B., HEUSER, G. F. & NORRIS, L. C. (1948). *J. Nutr.* **35**, 351
GLAZENER, E. W. & BRIGGS, G. M. (1948). *Poult. Sci.* **27**, 462
GLAZENER, E. W., MATTINGLY, J. P. & BRIGGS, G. M. (1946). *Poult. Sci.* **25**, 85
GLEDHILL, R. H. & SMITH, S. B. (1955). *Poult. Sci.* **34**, 942
GOGUS, K. A. & GRIMINGER, P. (1957). *Poult. Sci.* **36**, 1121
GOGUS, K. A. & GRIMINGER, P. (1959). *Poult. Sci.* **38**, 533
GOLDSTEIN, J. & SCOTT, M. L. (1956). *J. Nutr.* **60**, 349
GRAY, J. E., SNOEYENBOS, G. H. & REYNOLDS, I. M. (1954). *J. Am. vet. med. Ass.* **125**, 144
GRIMINGER, P. (1957). *Poult. Sci.* **36**, 1227
GRIMINGER, P. (1964). *Poult. Sci.* **43**, 1289

GRIMINGER, P. (1965a). *Poult. Sci.* **44**, 210
GRIMINGER, P. (1965b). *J. Nutr.* **87**, 337
GRIMINGER, P. (1966a). *Vitams Horm.* **24**, 605
GRIMINGER, P. (1966b). *Poult. Sci.* **45**, 849
GRIMINGER, P. & DONIS, O. (1960). *J. Nutr.* **70**, 361
GUNTHER, K. & TEKIN, C. (1964). *Arch Tierernähr.* **14**, 431
GUTZMANN, W. C. & DONOVAN, G. A. (1966). *Poult. Sci.* **45**, 1088
HARMS, R. H. & TUGWELL, R. L. (1956). *Poult. Sci.* **35**, 937
HARMS, R. H. & WALDROUP. P. W. (1963). *Poult. Sci.* **42**, 657
HARMS, R. H., WALDROUP, P. W. & COX, D. D. (1960). *Proc. Soc. exp. Biol. Med.* **105**, 230
HARMS, R. H., WALDROUP, P. W. & COX, D. D. (1962). *Poult. Sci.* **41**, 1836
HARRIS, P. L. & LUDWIG, M. I. (1949). *J. Biol. Chem.* **179**, 1111
HATHCOCK, J. N., SCOTT, M. L. & THOMPSON, J. N. (1968). *Proc. Soc. exp. Biol. Med.* **127**, 935
HEGSTED, D. M. (1946). *J. Nutr.* **32**, 467
HEGSTED, D. M., MILLS, R. C., BRIGGS, G. M., ELVEHJEM, C. A. & HART, E. B. (1942). *J. Nutr.* **23**, 175.
HEGSTED, D. M. & PERRY, R. L. (1948). *J. Nutr.* **35**, 411
HEGSTED, D. M. & RAO, M. N. (1945). *J. Nutr.* **30**, 367
HERTELENDY, F. & TAYLOR, T. G. (1965). *Br. Poult. Sci.* **6**, 339
HEUSER, G. F. & SCOTT, M. L. (1953). *Poult. Sci.* **32**, 137
HEUSER, G. F., WILGUS, H. S. & NORRIS, L. C. (1938). *Poult. Sci.* **17**, 105
HEYWANG, B. W. (1952). *Poult. Sci.* **31**, 294
HILL, C. H. & GARREN, H. W. (1957a). *Fedn Proc. Fedn Am. Socs exp. Biol.* **16**, 388
HILL, C. H. & GARREN, H. W. (1957b). *Proc. 4th Int. Congr. Nutr., Paris*, 244
HILL, C. H., GARREN, H. W., KELLY, J. W. & BARBER, C. W. (1955). *Proc. Soc. exp. Biol. Med.* **88**, 535
HILL, E. G. (1966). *J. Nutr.* **89**, 465
HILL, E. G., SILBERNICK, C. L. & MCMEANS, E. (1967). *Poult. Sci.* **46**, 523
HILL, F. W., NORRIS, L. W. & SCOTT, M. L. (1954). *Poult. Sci.* **33**, 1059
HILL, F. W., SCOTT, M. L., NORRIS, L. C. & HEUSER, G. F. (1961). *Poult. Sci.* **40**, 1245
HOGAN, A. G., RICHARDSON, L. R., PATRICK, H., O'DELL, B. L. & KEMPSTER, H. L. (1941). *Poult. Sci.* **20**, 180
HOPKINS, D. T. & NESHEIM, M. C. (1962a). *Proc. Cornell Nutr. Conf. Fd Mfrs*, 104
HOPKINS, D. T. & NESHEIM, M. C. (1962b). *Poult. Sci.* **41**, 1651
HOPKINS, D. T. & NESHEIM, M. C. (1967). *Poult. Sci.* **46**, 872
HOPKINS, D. T., WITTER, R. L. & NESHEIM, M. C. (1963). *Proc. Soc. exp. Biol. Med.* **114**, 82
HOWES, C. E. & HUTT, F. B. (1956). *Poult, Sci.* **35**, 1223.
HUTCHINGS, B. L., OLESON, J. J. & STOKSTAD, E. J. R. (1956). *J. biol. Chem.* **163**, 447
JENSEN, L. S. (1965). *Poult. Sci.* **44**, 1609
JENSEN, L. S., CARVER, J. S. & MCGINNIS, J. (1955). *Poult. Sci.* **34**, 1203
JENSEN, L. S. & MARTINSON, R. (1969). *Poult. Sci.* **48**, 222
JENSEN, L. S. & MRAZ, F. R. (1966). *J. Nutr.* **88**, 249
JOHNSON, E. L. (1954). *Poult. Sci.* **33**, 100
JOHNSON, E. L. (1955). *Poult. Sci.* **34**, 1013
JUKES, T. H. (1940). *J. Nutr.* **20**, 445
JUKES, T. H. & HEITMAN, H. (1940). *J. Nutr.* **19**, 21
JUKES, T. H. & MCELROY, L. W. (1943). *Poult. Sci.* **22**, 438
JUKES, T. H. & STOKSTAD, E. L. R. (1951). *J. Nutr.* **43**, 459
JUKES, T. H., STOKSTAD, E. L. R. & BELT, M. (1947). *J. Nutr.* **33**, 1
JUNGHERR, E. L. (1949). *Ann. N.Y. Acad. Sci.* **52**, 104
JUNGHERR, E. L. & PAPPENHEIMER, A. M. (1937-38). *Proc. Soc. exp. Biol. Med.* **37**, 520
KARB, B. (1967). *Arch. Geflügelk.* **31**, 399
KIRCHGESSNER, M. & FRIESECKE, H. (1963). *Arch. Geflügelk.* **27**, 412
KIRCHGESSNER, M. & MAIER, D. A. (1968a). *Arch. Tierernähr.* **18**, 300
KIRCHGESSNER, M. & MAIER, D. A. (1968b). *Arch. Tierernähr.* **18**, 309
KRATZER, F. H., BIRD, F. H., ASMUNDSON, V. S. & LEPKOVSKY, S. (1947). *Poult. Sci.* **26**, 453
KRATZER, F. H., DAVIS, P. N. & ABBOTT, UK (1956). *Poult. Sci.* **35**, 711

KRATZER, F. H., DAVIS, P. N., MARSHALL, B. J. & WILLIAMS, D. E. (1955). *Poult. Sci.* **34**, 68
KRATZER, F. H. & WILLIAMS, D. E. (1948). *Poult. Sci.* **27**. 518
KREHL, W. A. ELVEHJEM, C. A. & STRONG, F. M. (1944). *J. Biol. Chem.* **156**, 13
KRIEG, R. (1963). *Arch. Geflügelk*, **27**, 215
KRIEG, R. & LÖLIGER, H. CH. (1963). *Arch. Geflügelk*, **27**, 483
KUHNS, R. V. & ARSCOTT, G. H. (1969). *Poult. Sci.* **48**, 1646
KURNICK, A. A., HEYWANG, B. W., HULLETT, B. J., VAVICH, M. G. & REID, B. L. (1964). *Poult. Sci.* **43**, 1583
LAMOREUX, W. F. & HUTT, F. B. (1939). *J. agric. Res.* **58**, 307
LAMOREUX, W. F. & HUTT, F. B. (1948). *Poult. Sci.* **27**, 334
LANGER, B. W. & KRATZER, F. B. (1964). *Poult. Sci.* **43**, 127
LERNER, I. M. & BIRD, F. H. (1948). *Poult. Sci.* **27**, 342
LEUTSKAJA, Z. A. (1963). *Dokl. Akad. Nauk SSSR* **153**, 243
LILLIE, R. J. & BRIGGS, G. M. (1947). *Poult. Sci.* **26**, 295
LILLIE, R. J. COMBS, G. F. & BRIGGS, G. M. (1950). *Poult. Sci.* **29**, 115
LILLIE, R. J. & MENGE, H. (1968). *J. Nutr.* **95**, 311
MACHLIN, L. J. & SHALKOP, W. T. (1956). *J. Nutr.* **60**, 87
MAIER, D. A. & KIRCHGESSNER, M. (1967). *Arch Geflügelk.* **31**, 254
MANOUKAS, A. G., RINGROSE, R. C. & TEERI, A. E. (1968). *Poult. Sci.* **47**, 1836
MARCH, B. E. & BIELY, J. (1953). *Poult. Sci.* **32**, 768
MARCH, B. E. & BIELY, J. (1955). *Poult. Sci.* **34**, 39
MARCH, B. & BIELY, J. (1956a). *Poult. Sci.* **35**, 545
MARCH, B. & BIELY, J. (1956b). *Poult. Sci.* **35**, 550
MARCH, B. E. & BIELY, J. (1964). *Poult. Sci.* **43**, 393
MARIAKULANDAI, A. & McGINNIS, J. (1953). *Poult. Sci.* **32**, 3
MARION, J. E. & EDWARDS, H. M. (1964). *Poult. Sci.* **43**, 911
MARUSICH, W. L., ACKERMAN, G. & BAUERNFEIND, J. C. (1967). *Poult. Sci.* **46**, 541
MARUSICH, W. & BAUERNFEIND, J. C. (1963). *Poult. Sci.* **42**, 949
MATSCHINER, J. T. & DOISY, E. A. (1966). *J. Nutr.* **90**, 97
MAW, A. J. G. (1954). *Poult. Sci.* **33**, 216
MAYFIELD, H. L., ROEHM, R. R. & BEECKLER, A. F. (1955). *Poult. Sci.* **34**, 1106
McCHESNEY, E. W. (1943). *J. Nutr.* **26**, 81
McKITTRICK, D. S. (1947). *Archs Biochem*, **15**, 133
MEHNER, A., TORGES, H. G. & VOGT, H. (1965). *Arch. Geflügelk*, **29**, 356
MENGE, H. (1968). *J. Nutr.* **95**, 578
MENGE, H. (1970). *Poult. Sci.* **49**, 178
MENGE, H., CALVERT, C. C. & DENTON, C. A. (1965a). *J. Nutr.* **86**, 115
MENGE, H., CALVERT, C. C. & DENTON, C. A. (1965b). *J. Nutr*, **87**, 365
MENGE, H., MILLER, E. C. & DENTON, C. A. (1964). *Poult. Sci.* **43**, 164
MENGE, H. & RICHARDSON, G. V. (1968). *Poult. Sci.* **47**, 542
MILLER, D. L. & BALLOUN, S. L. (1967). *Poult. Sci.* **46**, 1503
MILLER, E. C., MENGE, H. & DENTON, C. A. (1963). *J. Nutr.* **80**, 431
MILLIGAN, J. L. & COMBS, G. F. (1950). *Poult. Sci.* **29**, 772
MITROVIC, M., MARUSICH, W. L. & DEUTSCH, D. (1969). *Poult. Sci.* **48**, 1633
MOTZOK, I. (1950). *Biochem, J.* **47**, 193
MOTZOK, I. & BRANION, H. D. (1948). *Poult Sci.* **27**, 482
MURPHY, R. R., HUNTER, J. E. & KNANDEL, H. C. (1936). *Bull. Pa agric. Exp. Stn* **334**
MUYTJENS, E. E. (1956). *Biochim. biophys. Acta* **20**, 553
NEAGLE, L. H., BLAYLOCK, L. G. & GOIHL, J. H. (1968). *Poult. Sci.* **47**, 174
NELSON, T. S. & NORRIS, L. C. (1959). *Poult. Sci.* **38**, 1094
NELSON, T. S. & NORRIS, L. C. (1960). *J. Nutr.* **72**, 137
NELSON, T. S. & NORRIS, L. C. (1961a). *Poult. Sci.* **40**, 392
NELSON, T. S. & NORRIS, L. C. (1961b). *J. Nutr.* **73**, 135
NESHEIM, M. C., CALVERT, C. C. & SCOTT, M. L. (1960). *Proc. Soc. exp. Biol. Med.* **104**, 783
NESHEIM, M. C. & SCOTT, M. L. (1958). *J. Nutr.* **65**, 601
NIR, I. & ASCARELLI, I. (1966). *Br. J. Nutr.* **20**, 41
NIR, I. & ASCARELLI, I. (1967a). *Br. J. Nutr.* **21**, 167
NIR, I. & ASCARELLI, I. (1967b). *Br. Poult. Sci.* **8**, 169
NOCKELS, C. F. & KIENHOLZ, E. W. (1966). *Poult. Sci.* **45**, 1111

NOCKELS, C. F. & KIENHOLZ, E. W. (1967). *J. Nutr.* **92**, 384

OLSEN, E. M., HARVEY, J. D., HILL, D. C. & BRANION, H. D. (1959a). *Poult. Sci.* **38**, 929

OLSEN, E. M., HARVEY, J. D., HILL, D. C. & BRANION, H. D. (1959b). *Poult. Sci.* **38**, 942

OLSEN, E. M., HILL, D. C. & BRANION, H. D. (1964). *Poult. Sci.* **43**, 1488

OTT, W. H. (1951). *Poult. Sci.* **30**, 86

OTT, W. H., DICKINSON, A. M. & VAN IDERSTINE, A. (1965). *Poult. Sci.* **44**, 920

OTTO, G. F., JESKE, H. A., FROST, D. V. & PERDUE, H. S. (1957). *Poult. Sci.* **36**, 1147

PADHI, P. & COMBS, G. F. (1965). *Poult. Sci.* **44**, 1405

PANDA, B. & COMBS, G. F. (1963). *Proc. Soc. exp. Biol. Med.* **113**, 530

PANDA, B., COMBS, G. F. & DEVOLT, H. M. (1964). *Poult. Sci.* **43**, 154

PANDE, P. G. & KRISHNAMURTY, D. (1959). *Poult. Sci.* **38**, 13

PAREDES, J. R. & GARCIA, T. P. (1959). *Poult. Sci* **38**, 3

PARRISH, D. B., ZIMMERMAN, R. A., SANFORD, P. E. & HUNG, E. (1963). *J. Nutr.* **79**, 9

PATRICK, H., BOUCHER, R. V., DUTCHER, R. A. & KNANDEL, H. C. (1942). *Poult. Sci.* **21**, 476

PATRICK, H., DARROW, M. I. & MORGAN, C. L. (1944). *Poult. Sci.* **23**, 146

PATTERSON, E. B., HUNT, J. R., VOHRA, F., BLAYLOCK. L. G. & MCGINNIS, J. (1956). *Poult. Sci.* **35**, 499

PEACOCK, R. G. & COMBS, G. F. (1969). *Poult. Sci.* **48**, 1857

PEREK, M. & KENDLER, J. (1963). *Br. Poult. Sci.* **4**, 191

PEREK, M. & SNAPIR, N. (1963). *Br. Poult. Sci.* **4**, 19

PETERSEN, C. F., LAMPMAN, C. E. & STAMBERG, O. E. (1947a). *Poult. Sci.* **26**, 180

PETERSEN, C. F., LAMPMAN, C. E. & STAMBERG, O. E. (1947b). *Poult. Sci.* **26**, 187

PETERSEN, C. F., WIESE, A. C., DAHLSTROM, R. V. & LAMPMAN, C. E. (1952). *Poult. Sci.* **31**, 129

PETERSEN, C. F., WIESE, A. C., MILNE. G. E. & LAMPMAN, C. E. (1953). *Poult. Sci.* **32**, 535

POLIN D., OTT, W. H., WYNOSKY, E. R. & PORTER, C. C. (1963). *Poult. Sci.* **42**, 925

POLIN, D., WYNOSKY, E. R. & PORTER, C. C. (1962). *Proc. Soc. exp. Biol. Med.* **110**, 844

PRICE, F. (1968). *Poult. Sci.* **47**, 1037

PUDELKIEWICZ, W. J., MATTERSON, L. D., POTTER, L. M., WEBSTER, L. & SINGSEN, E. P. (1960). *J. Nutr.* **71**, 115

PUDELKIEWICZ, W. J., WEBSTER, L., OLSON, G. & MATTERSON, L. D. (1964). *Poult. Sci.* **43**, 1157

QUILLIN, E. C., COMBS, G. F., CREEK, R. D. & ROMOSER, G. L. (1961). *Poult. Sci.* **40**, 639

RAMP, W. K. & THORNTON, P. A. (1966). *Proc. Soc. exp. Biol. Med.* **121**, 1248

RANDALL, C. J. (1964). *Vet. Bull.* **34**, 123

REID, B. L., HEYWANG, B. W., KURNICK, A. A., VAVICH, M. G. & HULETT, B. J. (1965). *Poult. Sci.* **44**, 446

REMP, D. G. & MARSHALL, I. H. (1938). *J. Nutr.* **15**, 525

RINGROSE, R. C., MANOUKAS, A. G., HINKSON, R. K. & TEERI, A. E. (1964). *Poult. Sci.* **43**, 1356

RINGROSE, R. C., MANOUKAS, A. G., HINKSON, R. & TEERI, A. E. (1965). *Poult. Sci.* **44**, 1053

ROBENALT, R. C. (1960). *Poult. Sci.* **39**, 354

ROBERTS, T. & FRITZ, J. C. (1968). *Poult. Sci.* **47**, 1711

ROBERTSON, E. I., DANIEL. L. J., FARMER, F. A., NORRIS, L. C. & HEUSER, G. F. (1946) *Proc. Soc. exp. Biol. Med.* **62**, 97

ROSS, E. & ADAMSON, L. (1961). *J. Nutr.* **74**, 329

RUSSELL, W. C., TAYLOR, M. W. & DERBY, J. V. (1947). *J. Nutr.* **34**, 621

SATTERFIELD, G. H., MOSELEY, M. A., GAUGER, H. C., HOLMES, A. D. & TRIPP, F. (1940). *Poult. Sci.* **19**, 337

SAVILLE, D. G., SOLVYNS, A. & HUMPHRIES, C. (1967). *Aust. vet J.* **43**, 346

SCHAEFER, A. E., SALMON, W. D. & STRENGTH, D. R. (1949). *Proc. Soc. exp. Biol. Med.* **71**, 202

SCHOLTYSSEK, S. (1963). *Arch. Geflügelk,* **27**, 48

Schweigert, B. S., German, H. L., Pearson, P. B. & Sherwood, R. M. (1948). *J. Nutr.* **35,** 89
Scott, H. M. (1955). *Feed Age,* no. 5, 40
Scott, M. L. (1953). *Poult. Sci.* **32,** 670
Scott, M. L. (1962a). *Nutr. Abstr. Rev.* **32,** 1
Scott, M. L. (1962b). *Vitams Horm.* **20,** 621
Scott, M. L. (1966). *Vitams Horm.* **24,** 633
Scott, M. L. (1968). *Feedstuffs, Minneap.* **40,** 24
Scott, M. L. & Calvert, C. C. (1962). *J. Nutr.* **77,** 105
Scott, M. L., Heuser, G. F. & Norris, L. C. (1948). *Poult. Sci.* **27,** 770
Scott, M. L., Hill. F. W., Norris, L. C., Dobson, D. C. & Nelson, T. S. (1955). *J. Nutr.* **56,** 387
Scott, M. L., Holm, E. R. & Reynolds, R. E. (1958). *Poult. Sci.* **37,** 1419
Scott, M. L, Holm, E. R. & Reynolds, R. E. (1959). *Poult. Sci.* **38,** 1344
Scott, M. L., Holm, E. R. & Reynolds, R. E. (1961). *Poult. Sci.* **40,** 1593
Scott, M. L., Norris, L. C., Heuser, G. F. & Nelson, T. S. (1955). *Poult. Sci.* **34,** 1220
Scrimshaw, N. S., Hutt, F. B. & Scrimshaw, N. W. (1945). *J. Nutr.* **30,** 375
Sherwood, D. H. & Briggs, G. M. (1951) *Poult. Sci.* **30,** 902
Sherwood, D. H. & Sloan, H. J. (1954). *Poult. Sci.* **33,** 1015
Shutze, J. V., Jensen. L. S. & McGinnis, J. (1962). *Poult. Sci.* **41,** 1846.
Siedler, A. J., Enzer, E. & Schweigert, B.S. (1956). *J. agric. Fd Chem.* **4,** 1023
Singh, S. P. & Donovan, G. A. (1966). *Poult. Sci.* **45,** 1124
Singsen, E. P., Bunnell, R. H., Matterson, L. D., Kozeff, A. & Jungherr, E. L. (1955). *Poult. Sci.* **34,** 262
Singsen, E. P., Matterson, L. D., Kozeff, A. & Decker, L. (1950). *Poult. Sci.* **29,** 780
Slinger, S. J., Pepper, W. F. & Evans, E. V. (1955). *Poult. Sci.* **34,** 1222
Slinger, S. J., Pepper, W. F. & Motzok, I. (1954). *J. Nutr.* **52,** 395
Slinger, S. J., Pepper, W. F. & Sibbald, I. R. (1962). *Poult. Sci.* **41,** 974
Squibb, R. L. (1964). *Poult. Sci.* **43,** 1443
Squibb, R. L., Braham, J. E. & Arroyave, G. (1958). *Poult. Sci.* **37,** 932
Squibb, R. L., Braham, J. E., Guzman, M. & Scrimshaw, N. S. (1955). *Poult. Sci.* **34,** 1054
Squibb, R. L. & Veros, H. (1961). *Poult. Sci.* **40,** 425
Stadelman, W. J., Boucher, R. V. & Callenbach, E. W. (1950). *Poult. Sci.* **29,** 146
Stoewsand, G. S. & Scott, M. L. (1961a). *Poult, Sci.* **40,** 1255
Stoewsand, G. S. & Scott, M. L. (1961b). *Proc. Soc. exp. Biol. Med.* **106,** 635
Stoewsand, G. S. & Scott, M. L. (1964a). *J. Nutr.* **82,** 139
Stoewsand, G. S. & Scott, M. L. (1964b). *J. Nutr.* **82,** 188
Stokstad, E. L. R., Jukes, T. H., Pierce, J., Page, A. C. & Franklin, A. L. (1949). *J. biol. Chem.* **180,** 647
Sturkie, P. D., Singsen, E. P., Matterson, L. D., Kozeff, A. & Jungherr, E. L. (1954). *Poult. Sci.* **33,** 1083
Sullivan, T. W., Heil, H. M. & Armintrout, M. E. (1967). *Poult. Sci.* **46,** 1560.
Sullivan, T. W. & Kingan, J. R. (1963). *Poult. Sci.* **42,** 1335
Sunde, M. L. & Bird, H. R. (1957). *Poult. Sci.* **36,** 34
Sunde, M. L., Cravens, W. W., Bruins, H. W., Elvehjem, C. A. & Halpin, J. G (1950). *Poult. Sci.* **29,** 220

Taylor, L. W. (1947). *Poult. Sci.* **26,** 372
Taylor, T. G., Morris. K. M. L. & Kirkley, J. (1968). *Br. J. Nutr.* **22,** 713
Thompson, J. N., Howell, J.McC., Pitt. E. A. J. & Houghton, C. I. (1965). *Nature, Lond.* **205,** 1006
Thornton, P. A. (1960a). *Poult. Sci.* **39** 440
Thornton, P. A. (1960b). *Poult. Sci.* **39,** 1072
Thornton, P. A. (1968). *Br. J. Mutr.* **22,** 77
Thornton, P. A. & Brownrigg, D. (1961). *J. Nutr.* **75,** 354
Thornton, P. A. & Moreng, R. E. (1959). *Poult. Sci.* **38,** 594
Thornton, P. A. & Shutze, J. V. (1960). *Poult. Sci* **39.** 192
Thornton, P. A., Shutze, J. V. & Moreng, R. E. (1957). *Poult. Sci.* **36,** 1164
Thornton, P. A. & Whittet, W. A. (1962). *Poult. Sci.* **41,** 32
Tiews, J. & Kring, P. L. (1962). *Int. Z. VitamForsch.* **32,** 258

TIEWS, J. & ZENTZ, C. (1967a). *Int. Z. VitamForsch*, **37**, 428
TIEWS, J. & ZENTZ, C. (1967b). *Z. Tierphysiol. Tierernähr. Futtermittelk*. **22**, 365
TUGWELL, R. L., STEPHENS, J. F. & HARMS, R. H. (1957). *Poult. Sci.* **36**, 1245
TURK, J. L. & McGINNIS, J. (1964). *Poult. Sci.* **43**, 1372
WAGSTAFF, R. K., DOBSON, D. C. & ANDERSON, J. O. (1961). *Poult. Sci.* **40**, 503
WAIBEL, P. E., KRISTA, L. M., ARNOLD, R. L., BLAYLOCK, L. G. & NEAGLE, L. H. (1969). *Poult. Sci.* **48**, 1979
WALDROUP, P. W., AMMERMAN, C. B. & HARMS, R. H. (1963). *Poult. Sci.* **42**, 982
WALDROUP, P. W., SIMPSON, C. F., COX. D. D. & HARMS, R. H. (1963). *Poult. Sci.* **42**, 274
WALDROUP, P. W., STEARNS, J. E., AMMERMAN, C. B. & HARMS, R. H. (1965). *Poult. Sci.* **44**, 543
WALSH, B. M., KINGAN, J. R. & SULLIVAN, T. W. (1963). *Poult. Sci.* **42**, 1316
WEST, J. W., CARRICK, C. W., HAUGE, S. M. & MERTZ, E. T. (1951). *Poult. Sci.* **30**, 880
WEST, J. W., CARRICK, C. W., HAUGE, S. M. & MERTZ, E. T. (1952). *Poult. Sci.* **31**, 479
WHITMORE, J. H., SULLIVAN, T. W. & GRACE, O. D. (1966). *Poult. Sci.* **45**, 1137
WIESE, A. C., PETERSEN, C. F., DAHLSTROM, R. V. & LAMPMAN, C. E. (1952). *Poult. Sci.* **31**, 851
WILSON, J. G. & TEEKELL, R. A. (1966). *Poult. Sci.* **45**, 980
WOLBACH, S. B. & HEGSTED, D. M. (1952). *Archs Path.* **54**, 1
YACOWITZ, H., MILLER, R. F., NORRIS, L. C. & HEUSER, G. F. (1952). *Poult. Sci.* **31**, 89
YOSHIDA, M., HOSHII, H. & MORIMOTO, H. (1966). *Poult. Sci.* **45**, 736
YOUNG, R. J., NORRIS, L. C. & HEUSER, G. F. (1955). *J. Nutr.* **55**, 353
ZACHARIAS, L., GOLDHABER, P. & KINSEY, V. E. (1950). *J. Nutr.* **42**, 359

CHAPTER 5

REQUIREMENTS FOR WATER

There is a considerable amount of information in the literature on water intake of fowls but it is of limited value as a guide to estimating water requirements because of the frequent absence of data on one or more of the many factors which can influence water intake. Because of variation in such factors as diet, egg production and environmental temperature, water requirements can vary greatly and no generally applicable figures are obtainable, However, since water restriction can have undesirable effects it is usually recommended that water should be available at all times. In the circumstances, the determination of water requirements for all combinations of conditions, even if feasible, would be largely an academic exercise.

ESTIMATES OF WATER INTAKE

Growing chickens

Information on the water intake of growing birds is contained in numerous reports, those with the most extensive data being summarised in Table 5.1.

Table 5.1
Water intake of growing chickens (ml/bird week)

Age (weeks)	Medway & Kare (1959)	Patrick & Ferrise (1962)	Kellerup, Parker & Arscott (1965)	Bierer, Eleazer & Barnett (1966)
1	192	104	141	144
2	290	209	277	248
3	380	372	431	—
4	552	626	590	—
5	—	667	694	718
6	584	807	780	926
7	—	885	903	—
8	847	953	908	—
9	—	1071	—	—

Adult birds

In addition to varying with the size of the bird (Medway and Kare, 1959) water intake is affected by breed (Favret, Lifschitz and Manso, 1967; Jull, 1949) and by sex. Jull (1949) estimated that for each egg produced, approximately 340 ml of water were required including body requirements. Lifschitz, German, Favret and Manso (1967) found the average intake of females to be some 80% greater than that of males kept under similar conditions, which they suggested was accounted for by the physiological activity associated with egg production

143

and the considerable amount of water contained in the egg. However, Anderson and Hill (1968) suggest that the increase in water intake at the onset of lay is in excess of that necessary to balance the increased output in the egg and that movement of water and electrolytes into the reproductive tract is also involved. The numerous references to water intake in the grower and layer stages cover a wide range of values (see Table 5.2). It is therefore not surprising to find that recommendations for water allowances are usually couched in very general terms such as "lb per bird per year" or "gallons per 100 birds per day".

Table 5.2

Water intake of adult fowls

Reference	Type of bird	Average intake (ml/day)
Heywang (1941)	White Leghorns hens	225
	Rhode Island Red hens	247
Jull (1949)	First year layers	
	180 eggs/year	164
	215 ,, ,,	193
	230 ,, ,,	211
	240 ,, ,,	224
Sturkie (1956)	White Leghorn layers	216
Maxwell & Lyle (1957)	1-year-old layers	326
Wilson, McNally & Ota (1957)	White Leghorn pullets	168–224
Dixon (1958)	White Leghorn hens	325
Tyler (1958)	Rhode Island Red x Light Sussex hens	292
Medway & Kare (1959)	White Leghorn pullets, 16 weeks old	174
	White Leghorn pullets, 32 weeks old	496
Sturkie & Joiner (1959)	Hens (unspecified)	303
Krista, Carlson & Olson (1961)	White Leghorn pullets	145–194
Lifschitz, German, Favret & Manso (1967)	White Leghorns, 10 months old, male	91 ± 15
	White Leghorns, 10 months old, female	167 ± 17
Anderson & Hill (1968)	Thornber 606	
	Pre-lay (18 weeks)	102 ± 7
	Lay (48 weeks)	202 ± 16
	Post-lay (66 weeks)	108 ± 19
	Second lay (78 weeks)	214 ± 48
Wood-Gush & Horne (1970)	Brown Leghorn layers	165–420

144

Diet

The amount, nature and composition of the diet have all been shown to influence water intake. Thus Sykes (1955) suggested that for poultry the ratio of water to dry matter intake was 3:1. Ratios quoted in the literature again vary considerably (see Table 5.3) and Tyler (1958) could find no fixed ratio between daily water and food intake.

Table 5.3
Water intake as a function of feed consumed

Reference	Type of Bird	g water/g feed
Kare & Biely (1948)	Baby chicks	1·70
Barott & Pringle (1949)	Chicks, 18 to 32 days	1·75
Glista & Scott (1949)	Chicks, 0 to 8 weeks	1·95–2·24
Barott & Pringle (1949)	Chicks, 1 to 18 days	1·55
Patrick (1955)	Broiler chicks over 5 weeks	1·5–2·6
Wilson, McNally & Ota (1957)	White Leghorn pullets	2·1
Dixon (1958)	White Leghorn hens	3
Medway & Kare (1959)	White Leghorn growers	2·1–3·6
Sturkie & Joiner (1959)	Hens (unspecified)	2·1
Longhouse, Ota & Ashby (1960)	Laying hens	1·7–2·5
Ross (1960)	Chicks, 1 week old	2·0
Kondo & Ross (1962)	Chicks (unspecified)	2·3
Patrick & Ferrise (1962)	Chicks, 1 to 9 weeks	1·11–1·64
Kellerup, Parker & Arscott (1965)	Broiler chicks 1 to 8 weeks	1·16–1·64
Anderson & Hill (1968)	Thornber 606	
	Pre-lay (18 weeks)	1·21 ± 0·02
	Lay (48 weeks)	2·04 ± 0·20
	Post-lay (66 weeks)	1·33 ± 0·20
	Second lay (78 weeks)	1·99 ± 0·60

Both the physical and the chemical composition of the diet have been said to affect water intake. Patten and Rouls (1938) showed that pellet fed chicks consumed about 30% more water than mash fed chicks. Following an observation that feeding of grain or grain plus mash instead of mash only reduced the amount of moisture in poultry litter, Eley and Hoffman (1949) studied the relationship of feed particle size to water consumption and excretion by 7-week-old broiler chicks. Using fine, medium and course mash and pelleted mash, they failed to demonstrate any significant effect on water or feed consumption or weight.

Arscott, McCluskey and Parker (1958) in reporting a study of the effects of substituting barley for maize in the diet claimed that pelleting increased water consumption of broiler chicks by about 12% (range −2% to 29%); but Arscott and Rose (1960) in a further study of the use of barley in high efficiency broiler rations found that pelleting of the barley rations led to only a slight (2½%) and not significant increase in water consumption.

Variations in the chemical composition of the diet and particularly in the protein and salt content would appear to have more definite effects. In a study of the relationship between protein intake and water excretion, James and Wheeler (1949) used 3 diets differing essentially in protein content (viz. 150, 200 and 250 g/kg) as a result of varying the corn and soya bean meal content. Using 12-week-old Rhode Island Red males and females they found that the amount of water consumed as well as the amount of droppings varied almost directly with the percentage of protein in the diet while the amount of feed consumed and the water content of the droppings were not affected. They assumed from these results that greater amounts of water were needed for the metabolism of protein than for carbohydrates and fats. Glista and Scott (1949) using day-old female chicks fed on rations containing 210 g protein/kg but with varying levels of soya bean meal (75, 150 and 300 g/kg) found that only at the highest level did they get an exaggerated water consumption, the ratio of water to food consumed being 1·95, 2·01 and 2·41 to 1 respectively. However, Patrick (1955) using a variety of protein sources in place of maize meal to raise the protein content of the diet from 210 to 270 g/kg found that casein in particular and also some samples of meat scraps, fish meal and cottonseed meal, slightly reduced water intake. Arscott, McCluskey and Parker (1958) feeding broiler chicks over the first 8 to 9 weeks of life on diets which contained varying amounts of maize, barley and stabilised animal fat, showed an increase in water consumption of approximately 8% and 12·5% where barley replaced one half and all of the maize respectively. Patrick and Ferrise (1962) in a study of the water requirements of broilers also looked at the effects of dietary fat and protein, and using finisher rations of varying protein content (210, 240 and 280 g/kg) they found that the highest level of protein produced both the highest water intake and the highest water to food ratio; and that the effect was greatest when the increased protein percentage was produced by adding soya bean meal to the diet.

Water consumption can be affected by dietary minerals, particularly sodium chloride which has been extensively investigated because of its potential toxicity. Kare and Biely (1948) found that water intake per gram of feed consumed increased from 1·70 ml on a basal diet containing 1·8 g salt/kg to 8·71 ml when 80 g salt/kg was added. Krista, Carlson and Olson (1961) presented the results

Table 5.4

The effect on fluid intake of adding salt to the drinking water (Krista, Carlson and Olson, 1961)

Added salt g/litre	Average daily water intake (ml)
0	204
4	240
7	376
12	476

of studies on the effects of graded levels of salt solution up to 12 g/litre on day-old chicks (see Table 5.4). A concentration of 4 g/litre led to increased fluid consumption and the intake was increased further at 7 g/litre, which level also reduced growth rate and increased mortality.

Other minerals can also have an effect. Thus Kondo and Ross (1962) investigating the effects of some constituents of molasses on the water metabolism of chicks found that adding potassium and magnesium salts to chick rations resulted in increased water consumption; and that the increase appeared to be directly related to the amounts of sodium or potassium or both in the feed. Molasses itself also appeared to increase water consumption to an extent which was not wholly accounted for by its sugar content. On the other hand Sturkie (1956) found that 10 g zinc sulphate/1 in the drinking water tended to decrease the consumption though whether this was due to unpalatability or toxicity was not resolved. Kare and Pick (1960) using unspecified "offensive" flavours in an attempt to reduce acceptability reported that very high levels had to be used before a decrease in consumption was noticed. When strong acids or alkalis were added to drinking water Fuerst and Kare (1962) found that the intake of young chickens remained relatively constant between pH2 and pH10 though there was definite reduction outside that range.

Temperature

As with other species, birds exposed to high environmental temperatures which increase respiratory water loss might be expected to consume more water. Wilson (1948) reported that the water consumption of White Leghorn pullets at 35°C was double that at 21°C. However, Wilson, McNally and Ota (1957) using White Leghorn pullets kept at temperatures ranging from 35°C to −3°C found that only at the extremes of the range did water consumption differ markedly from controls kept in an unheated room where the temperature decreased seasonally from 25°C to around 10°C and from similar birds kept in a respiration calorimeter at a constant temperature of 18°C (Table 5.5).

Table 5.5
Effect of environmental temperature on water consumption of laying pullets
(Wilson, McNally and Ota, 1957)

| Period | Experimental birds | | Unheated controls | | Constant temperature controls (18°C) |
	Temperature °C	Water intake g/day	Temperature °C	Water intake g/day	Water intake, g/day
A	35	229	25	184	197
B	30	221	25	194	198
C	24	206	24	214	207
D	18	207	19·5	207	182
E	13	226	13	217	224
F	8	229	12	259	214
G	2	194	12	229	206
H	−3	150	10	197	168

Tyler (1958) using Rhode Island Red × Light Sussex hens housed in metabolism cages with a temperature range of 11·5°C to 18°C found that temperature had practically no influence on either water intake or water loss. Smith (1972) found that White Leghorn hybrid pullets kept at 32°C drank significantly more water than those kept at 24°C. Similar pullets kept at 38°C initially consumed significantly more water than those kept at 24°C, but this increase was not maintained over the three week observation period when food consumption and egg production also declined.

Enos, Moreng and Whittet (1967) studied the effects of different types of shade at high ambient temperatures (around 30°C) on turkeys between 10 and 22 weeks of age and noted an increase in water consumption resulting from the absence of shade.

WATER RESTRICTION

It is frequently assumed that the voluntary intake of water supplied *ad libitum* gives a measure of water requirement and it is of interest, therefore, to consider the effects of water restriction, partial and complete, which have been reported in a number of papers (Bierer, Eleazer and Roebuck, 1965; Enos, Moreng and Whittet, 1967; Lepkovsky, Chari-Bitron, Lyman and Dimick, 1960; Maxwell and Lyle, 1957; Scheiber, Dziuk and Duke, 1969). The most extensive data are provided by Kellerup, Parker and Arscott (1965) who studied the effects of restricting the water consumption of broiler chickens between 1 and 8 weeks of age by 10%, 20%, 30%, 40%, and 50% of the amount consumed by those with water always available. Though the mortality rate was not significantly affected by any of the levels of water restriction, they found that body weight and feed consumption decreased with each increment of water restriction, and that reducing water intake by 20% or more had a deleterious effect on the feed conversion ratio. They concluded that for all practical purposes the water requirement of these broiler chicks approximated to the amount consumed by the controls given water *ad libitum*. Lei and Slinger (1970) also reported lowered performance efficiency in young chicks under conditions of reduced water intake.

NOTE ON FEED ADDITIVES

It is becoming increasingly common to include substances in the diet which are not nutrients but which in some way enhance production. These are referred to here as "feed additives". As these substances are not nutrients they do not fall strictly within the subject of this review. However, it is considered relevant to indicate the range of substances that may be included in poultry diets as feed additives. Some have been added to promote growth (antibiotics and other antibacterial substances); others to modify growth through an effect on hormone levels (oestrogen, thyroid depressants); others are used to increase the acceptability of the diet (appetisers), or to alleviate the effects of adverse environmental factors (tranquillisers, "anti-stress" agents) or to counteract disease (coccidiostats) or toxic effects of fungi in the diet (mycostats). Others are included to control reproduction (moult inducers), increase the storage life of the feeding stuff (antioxidants), ease feed manufacture and handling of formed feeds (binders), or modify the final product (yolk pigments).

It is evident on considering these groups of substances that their relation to the diet varies. For most, the diet is merely a convenient vehicle for administration of the substance while for a few (growth promoters and antioxidants) there is some degree of interaction with the diet.

REFERENCES

ANDERSON, R. S. & HILL, K. J. (1968). *Proc. Nutr. Soc.* **27**, 3A
ARSCOTT, G. H., MCCLUSKEY, W. H. & PARKER, J. E. (1958). *Poult. Sci.* **37**, 117
ARSCOTT, G. H. & ROSE, R. J. (1960). *Poult. Sci.* **39**, 93
BAROTT, H. G. & PRINGLE, E. M. (1949). *J. Nutr.* **37**, 153
BIERER, B. W., ELEAZER, T. H. & ROEBUCK, D. E. (1965). *Poult. Sci.* **44**, 768
BIERER, B. W., ELEAZER, T. H. & BARNETT, B. D. (1966). *Poult. Sci.* **45**, 1045
DIXON, J. M. (1958). *Poult. Sci.* **37**, 410
ELEY, C. P. & HOFFMAN, E. (1949). *Poult. Sci.* **28**, 215
ENOS, H. L., MORENG, R. E. & WHITTET, W. A. (1967). *Poult. Sci.* **46**, 1412
FAVRET, E. A., LIFSCHITZ, E. & MANSO, F. (1967). *Boll. Genet. Inst. Fitotec, Castolar*
FUERST, W. F. & KARE, M. R. (1962). *Poult. Sci.* **41**, 71
GLISTA, W. A. & SCOTT, H. M. (1949). *Poult. Sci.* **28**, 747
HEYWANG, B. W. (1941). *Poult. Sci.* **20**, 184
JAMES, F. C. & WHEELER, R. S. (1949). *Poult. Sci.* **28**, 465
JULL, M. A. (1949). *Wld's Poult. Sci. J.* **5**, 29
KARE, M. R. & BIELY, J. (1948). *Poult. Sci.* **27**, 751
KARE, M. R. & PICK, H. L. (1960). *Poult. Sci.* **39**, 697
KELLERUP, S. U., PARKER, J. W. & ARSCOTT, G. H. (1965). *Poult. Sci.* **44**, 78
KONDO, A. K. & ROSS, E. (1962). *Poult. Sci.* **41**, 1132
KRISTA, L. M., CARLSON, C. W. & OLSON, O. E. (1961). *Poult. Sci.* **40**, 938
LEI, K. Y. & SLINGER, S. J. (1970). *Can. J. Anim. Sci.* **50**, 288
LEPKOVSKY, S., CHARI-BITRON, A., LYMAN, R. L. & DIMICK, M. K. (1960). *Poult. Sci.* **39**, 390
LIFSCHITZ, E., GERMAN, O., FAVRET, E. A. & MANSO, F. (1967). *Poult. Sci.* **46**, 1021
LONGHOUSE, A. D., OTA, H. & ASHBY, W. (1960). *Agric. Engng, St. Joseph, Mich.* **41**, 567
MALIK, D. D. (1966). *J. Res. Ludhiana*, **3**, 443
MAXWELL, B. F. & LYLE, J. B. (1957). *Poult. Sci.* **36**, 921
MEDWAY, W. & KARE, M. R. (1959). *Poult. Sci.* **38**, 631
PATRICK, H. (1955). *Poult. Sci.* **34**, 155
PATRICK, H. & FERRISE, A. (1962). *Poult. Sci.* **41**, 1363
PATTEN, J. W. & ROULS, L. A. (1938). *Feedstuffs, Minneap.* Oct. 1, 12
ROSS, E. (1960). *Poult. Sci.* **39**, 999
SCHEIBER, A. R., DZIUK, H. E. & DUKE, G. E. (1969). *Poult. Sci.* **48**, 2179
SMITH, A. J. (1972). *Rhod. J. agric. Res.* **10**, 31
STURKIE, P. D. (1956). *Poult. Sci.* **35**, 1123
STURKIE, P. D. & JOINER, W. P. (1959). *Poult. Sci.* **38**, 30
SYKES, J. F. (1955). *USDA Yearbook of Agric.*, 14
TYLER, C. (1958). *J. agric. Sci., Camb.* **51**, 237
WILSON, W. O. (1948). *Poult. Sci.* **27**, 686
WILSON, W. O., MCNALLY, E. H. & OTA, H. (1957). *Poult. Sci.* **36**, 1254
WOOD-GUSH, D. G. M. & HORNE, A. R. (1970). *Br. Poult. Sci.* **11**, 459

CHAPTER 6

SUMMARY OF REQUIREMENTS

The nutrient requirements of the main classes of domestic poultry, as indicated by the evidence reviewed in the previous chapters, are summarised in Tables 6.1 and 6.2.

The values listed are best estimates of the minimal amounts needed in the diet to support maximal growth, egg production or hatchability. These estimates do not incorporate margins to allow for uncertainty in the quantities present in the feed at manufacture, for losses during storage or for increased requirements due to special factors such as disease or low feed intake.

It is common practice to feed substantially more than the minimal requirement levels of many of the vitamins and trace minerals, on the grounds that the cost is slight and that this is the simplest way to ensure that the diet is adequately fortified to meet any adverse circumstances that may arise. In the case of the major minerals and the amino acids the same arguments do not apply. There is a substantial cost incurred in formulating to provide levels of amino acids higher than those stated in the Tables. If circumstances arise in which the estimated requirements do not quite support maximum output, the consequential loss of economic return is small in relation to the cost of routinely supplying levels in excess of the estimated requirements. The provision of minerals in excess of the minimum requirements will tend to reduce the efficiency of utilization of the diet as a whole, but small surpluses have no adverse effects on production. The fuller tables in Chapter 3 give suitable ranges for most of the major minerals and where practicable, diets should be formulated to provide mineral concentrations within these ranges.

The following notes are a guide to some of the restrictions which should be placed on the use of the requirement values in Tables 6.1 and 6.2. For a full discussion of the factors which affect each estimate of requirement the reader is referred to earlier Chapters.

Energy There is no "required" concentration of ME in the diet for any class of poultry, since satisfactory performance can be achieved over a wide range of energy levels. The tables therefore give a reference level, which is approximately in the middle of the range that is economically feasible in the UK. The significance of this "assumed dietary ME" level is that it provides a standard to which the requirements for amino acids and the major minerals can be related. It is recommended that, when formulating diets with energy concentrations above or below the standards assumed, the requirements for amino acids, and the major minerals and vitamins should be increased or decreased proportionately. In the case of growing and adult fowls, requirements for these nutrients should be adjusted in inverse proportion to the anticipated feed intake.

Protein and amino acids The minimum level of nitrogen required in a diet has not been well defined for any class of poultry and the estimates of crude protein given in the Tables are likely to be above the true minimum values. When diets based on practical feedingstuffs are formulated to meet the specified amino acid levels the total crude protein contents will almost always exceed the tentative estimates of minimum requirement.

150

Table 6.1
Summary of the nutrient requirements of fowls, expressed as dietary concentrations. Figures in italics are tentative estimates only

		0 to 4 weeks	4 to 8 weeks	Growing pullets	Laying pullets	Breeding pullets
Assumed ME content of diet	{ Mcal/kg	3·1	3·1			
	{ MJ/kg	13	13			
Assumed feed intake	g/day			75	110	110
Crude protein	g/kg	*188*	*156*	*107*	*165**	*165**
Arginine	,,	10·3	7·6	6·0	5·1	5·1
Glycine + Serine	,,	14·0	10·2	8·0	?	?
Histidine	,,	4·8	3·6	2·8	1·7	1·7
Isoleucine	,,	8·5	6·4	4·9	5·5	5·5
Leucine	,,	14·7	10·7	8·4	6·8	6·8
Lysine	,,	11·0	8·0	6·3	7·5	7·5
Methionine	,,	4·8	3·6	2·8	3·5	3·5
Methionine + Cystine	,,	9·2	6·7	5·2	4·7	4·7
Phenylalanine	,,	8·5	6·4	4·9	3·9	3·9
Phenylalanine + Tyrosine	,,	15·8	11·6	9·1	7·0	7·0
Threonine	,,	7·4	5·3	4·2	3·6	3·6
Tryptophan	,,	2·1	1·5	1·2	1·7	1·7
Valine	,,	9·8	7·1	5·6	5·5	5·5
Calcium	g/kg	12	7·5	4	35	35
Non-phytin phosphorus	,,	4·7			3·5	3·5
Total phosphorus	,,		6·0	3·0		
Magnesium	,,	0·4	0·4	0·4	0·4	0·4
Sodium	,,	1·5	1·2	0·7	1·0	1·0
Chloride	,,	1·4	*1·1*	*0·6*	*0·9*	0·9
Potassium	,,	2·5	2·5	2·5	2·5	2·5
Copper	mg/kg	4				
Iodine	,,	0·4				0·2
Iron	,,	75				
Manganese	,,	50	*50*	*50*	30	50
Zinc	,,	40	*50*	*50*	*50*	60
Vitamin A	i.u./kg	1320	1320		2700	2700
Vitamin D₃	,,	400	400		600	600
Vitamin E	,,	*15*			?	?
Vitamin K₁	mg/kg	0·5			*1·0*	*1·0*
Thiamin	,,	1·0			1·25	?
Riboflavin	,,	4·0			2·5	4·0
Nicotinic acid	,,	28			8	10
Pantothenic acid	,,	10			1·5	6·5
Pyridoxine	,,	3·5			2·0	4·0
Biotin	,,	0·15				
Folic acid	,,	1·5			0·3	0·5
Vitamin B₁₂	,,	0·02†			?	0·002
Choline	,,	1300			600	1100
Linoleic acid	g/kg	10	10	*10*	12‡	2§

* These protein and amino acid requirements are for an egg output of 50 g/hen day.
† Assumes negligible reserves at hatching.
‡ Requirement for maximum egg weight for pullets reared on conventional diets.
§ Requirement for maximum hatchability.

151

Table 6.2

Summary of the nutrient requirements of turkeys, ducks, geese, pheasants and Japanese quail, expressed as dietary concentrations. Figures in italics are tentative estimates only

		Turkey poults	Turkey growers	Breeding turkeys	Ducklings	Goslings	Pheasant chicks	Japanese quail
Assumed ME content of diet	Mcal/kg	3·0	2·95		3·1	2·65		
	MJ/kg	12·6	12·3		12·8	11·1		
Crude protein	g/kg	280	220	*120*	230			
Arginine	,,	13·0	10·4		8·4	8·5		
Glycine + Serine	,,	9·0	7·2		11·3	11·4		
Histidine	,,	5·0	4·0		3·9	4·0		
Isoleucine	,,	9·0	7·2		6·9	7·0		
Leucine	,,	14·0	11·2		11·8	12·0		
Lysine	,,	13·0	10·4		8·9	9·0		
Methionine	,,	5·0	3·8		3·9	4·0		
Methionine + Cystine	,,	8·0	6·4		7·4	7·5		
Phenylalanine	,,	8·0	6·4		6·9	7·0		
Phenylalanine + Tyrosine	,,	14·0	11·2		12·8	13·0		
Threonine	,,	9·0	7·2		5·9	6·0		
Tryptophan	,,	2·2	1·8		1·7	1·7		
Valine	,,	10·0	8·0		7·9	8·0		
Calcium	g/kg	8	5	25	5·6	4	10	5
Non-phytin phosphorus	,,	6·5	5	5		4·6	8	4
Total phosphorus	,,							
Magnesium	,,							
Sodium	,,	0·45	0·45	0·45	0·5		0·85	
Chloride	,,	1·75	1·75	1·75			1·1	
Potassium	,,	4·4	4·4	4·4				
Copper	mg/kg							
Iodine	,,							
Iron	,,	75						
Manganese	,,	50					75	
Zinc	,,	70		100			60	

(continued on next page)

152

Table 6.2 (*continued*)

		Turkey poults	Turkey growers	Breeding turkeys	Ducklings	Goslings	Pheasant chicks	Japanese quail
Vitamin A	i.u./kg	1760		2700	?	?	?	
Vitamin D$_3$	,,	900		2000	300	300	1100	
Vitamin E	,,	15		60	?	?	?	
Vitamin K$_1$	mg/kg	1·5		?	?	?	0·06	
Thiamin	,,	2·0		?	?	?	?	
Riboflavin	,,	3·5		3·5	4·0	?	?	
Nicotinic acid	,,	35		16	25	65	65	
Pantothenic acid	,,	10·5		?	11	?	?	
Pyridoxine	,,	4·0		?	2·5	?	?	
Biotin	,,	0·25		0·2	?	?	?	
Folic acid	,,	1·5		0·7	?	?	?	
Vitamin B$_{12}$	,,	0·004		?	?	?	?	
Choline	g/kg	1500		1350	?	?	1400	
Linoleic acid	,,			12	?	?	?	

Minerals The requirements for magnesium and potassium can be ignored, except when formulating diets from purified ingredients. Where a range of requirements for calcium, phosphorus, sodium or chloride has been given in Table 3.6 the median value has been entered in the summary tables. The trace mineral requirements are estimates of minimum values and may safely be exceeded (see Table 3.13 for toxic levels of these minerals). A common practice is to include a supplement in the diet which will provide the requirement level for each of the trace minerals, ignoring the substantial contribution made by the natural ingredients in the diet.

Vitamins The extent to which vitamins added to the diet may be destroyed before use depends very much on the composition of the diet, the length and manner of storage and the form of the added vitamins. It is therefore not possible to prescribe any general rule about the amounts which should be added above the minimum requirement to allow for such losses. The requirement for vitamin E is particularly difficult to define, since the animal's need for the vitamin is profoundly affected by the presence or absence of oxidizing agents in the diet and the presence or absence of antioxidants other than vitamin E.